2022
CROSSWORD A DAY

No. 1
Saturday January 1st 2022

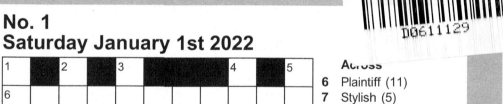

Across

6 Plaintiff (11)
7 Stylish (5)
8 Red colour (5)
9 Flexible (7)
12 Ruin (5)
13 Piece of land (5)
14 ~~ive~~ (11)

D0611129

First published in 2021 by
Clarity Media Ltd
www.clarity-media.co.uk

Puzzles created by Dan Moore

About Clarity Media
Clarity Media are a leading provider of a huge range of puzzles for adults and children. For more information on our services, please visit us at www.pzle.co.uk. For information on purchasing puzzles for publication, visit us at www.clarity-media.co.uk

Puzzle Magazines
If you enjoy the puzzles in this book, then you may be interested in our puzzle magazines. We have a very large range of magazines that you can download and print yourself in PDF format at our Puzzle Magazine site. For more information, take a look at www.puzzle-magazine.com

Online Puzzles
If you prefer to play puzzles online, please take a look at the Puzzle Club website, at www.thepuzzleclub.com

We also have more puzzle books available at
www.puzzle-book.co.uk

Contents

No. 1
Saturday January 1st 2022

Across
1 Holds on tightly (6)
4 Apex (4)
7 Ringo ___ : one of the Beatles (5)
8 Vaulted (5)
9 Turns around (on a chair) (7)
11 Opposite of later (7)
13 Looks good on (5)
14 Climbing shrubs (5)
15 Grain that grows into a new plant (4)
16 Concurs (6)

Down
1 Estimates the price of (5)
2 Creative (11)
3 Horticulturists (9)
5 Showing a desire to win (11)
6 ___ Izzard: stand-up comedian (5)
8 Taking weapons away from (9)
10 Clenched hands (5)
12 Flowers (5)

No. 2
Sunday January 2nd 2022

Across
1 Felts (anag) (5)
5 Musical instrument (5)
6 Moves up and down on water (4)
8 Novelty (7)
10 Allowance given to children (6,5)
11 Time between events (7)
12 Tablet (4)
14 Crevices (5)
15 Mingle with something else (5)

Down
1 High ball in tennis (3)
2 Act of making something (11)
3 Patriotism (11)
4 Domestic beasts of burden (7)
7 Plaited lock of hair (7)
9 Choices (7)
13 SI unit of illuminance (3)

No. 3
Monday January 3rd 2022

Across
1. Transitory (9)
5. Mischievous (6)
7. Freezes over (4)
8. Motor-driven revolving spindle (7)
11. Shuns (7)
14. Couple (4)
15. Sailing vessels (6)
16. Concerns; appeals (9)

Down
1. A curse; wicked look (4,3)
2. Pertaining to the liver (7)
3. Assumed name (5)
4. Bate (anag) (4)
6. Progress (7)
9. Comes into contact with (7)
10. Goddess of retribution (7)
12. Exchange (4)
13. Wading bird (5)

No. 4
Tuesday January 4th 2022

Across
1. Call to mind (4)
3. Amusingly eccentric (6)
7. Adult insect (5)
9. Cancel (5)
10. Multiplied threefold (7)
11. Become wrinkled (7)
13. Streamlined (5)
14. Legal process (5)
15. Going out with (6)
16. Matured (4)

Down
1. Young bird (5)
2. Semi-transparent (11)
4. Astonishment (9)
5. Not in agreement (11)
6. Plied (anag) (5)
8. Unreserved in speech (9)
11. Enclosed (5)
12. Lubricated (5)

No. 5
Wednesday January 5th 2022

Across

- **3** Long strips of cloth (6)
- **6** Distinguishing characteristic (5)
- **7** Illustrated material (7)
- **9** Impair (5)
- **12** Change in appearance (11)
- **14** Summed together (5)
- **15** Type of pheasant (7)
- **17** Bring down (5)
- **18** Amount of money left in a will (6)

Down

- **1** Written law (7)
- **2** Docking facilities for boats (7)
- **3** Current state of affairs (6,3)
- **4** In what way (3)
- **5** Ride the waves (4)
- **8** Normally; usually (9)
- **10** Reduced in scope or length (3-4)
- **11** Newspaper audience (7)
- **13** Meat from a calf (4)
- **16** Pear-shaped fruit (3)

No. 6
Thursday January 6th 2022

Across

- **1** Crazy (informal) (4)
- **3** Performing on stage (6)
- **7** Snake (5)
- **9** Cuban folk dance (5)
- **10** Person of high rank (7)
- **11** Decimal (anag) (7)
- **13** Negatively charged ion (5)
- **14** Smells strongly (5)
- **15** From Denmark (6)
- **16** Church song (4)

Down

- **1** Walks awkwardly (5)
- **2** Collection (11)
- **4** Herb (9)
- **5** Instantly (11)
- **6** Very serious (5)
- **8** Disagreements (9)
- **11** Kind of beet (5)
- **12** Substance exuded by some trees (5)

No. 7
Friday January 7th 2022

Across
1 Drying substance (9)
6 Doctor (5)
7 Cover with liquid (5)
9 A ripple (anag) (7)
12 Started an essay again (7)
16 Microscopic fungus (5)
17 Make fun of someone (5)
18 Use violence against (6-3)

Down
2 Froth of soap and water (4)
3 Chocolate powder (5)
4 Greek writer of fables (5)
5 Murky (6)
6 Stingy (7)
8 Golfing measure of distance (7)
10 Place (3)
11 Pinches sharply (6)
13 Semiaquatic mammal (5)
14 Consumed (of food) (5)
15 Main island of Indonesia (4)

No. 8
Saturday January 8th 2022

Across
1 Brown nut (5)
5 Connection; link (3-2)
6 Exclamation of relief (4)
8 Two-wheeled vehicle (7)
10 Eternal (11)
11 Where artwork is displayed (7)
12 Strict (4)
14 Cage for small pets (5)
15 Wide-awake (5)

Down
1 Young dog (3)
2 Coarse cotton gauze (11)
3 Serving to inform (11)
4 Endure (7)
7 Competition (7)
9 Distances (7)
13 Encountered (3)

No. 9
Sunday January 9th 2022

Across

1 How fast you may legally travel (5,5)
6 Barrier between rooms (4)
7 Saturated with liquid (6)
8 Moral excellence (6)
9 Opposite of hit (4)
11 Ooze or leak slowly (4)
13 Apathetic person (informal) (6)
15 Mustang; wild horse (6)
17 Tardy (4)
18 Resembling jelly (10)

Down

2 Supply (7)
3 White heron (5)
4 Polite address for a woman (5)
5 Foot extremity (3)
7 Use (anag) (3)
10 Japanese massage technique (7)
12 Committee (5)
13 Place where one sees animals (3)
14 Large fruit with pulpy flesh (5)
16 Floor mat (3)

No. 10
Monday January 10th 2022

Across

3 Mottled marking (6)
6 Select group of people (5)
7 Operating doctor (7)
9 Big (5)
12 One who presides over a meeting (11)
14 Small drum (5)
15 Writing fluid holder (7)
17 Military opponent (5)
18 Jams tight (6)

Down

1 Think deeply about (7)
2 Active during the day (7)
3 Violate (9)
4 Short cylindrical piece of wood (3)
5 Greek god of love (4)
8 Looks like (9)
10 Into parts (7)
11 Word opposite in meaning to another (7)
13 Was aware of; understood (4)
16 Roll of bank notes (3)

No. 11
Tuesday January 11th 2022

Across

1 Copying machine (10)
6 Cut very short (of hair) (4)
7 Desired (6)
8 Less tame (6)
9 Loud cry (4)
11 Low in pitch (4)
13 Superior of a nunnery (6)
15 On the beach; on land (6)
17 Takes to court (4)
18 Roughness (of water) (10)

Down

2 Country whose capital is Kiev (7)
3 Fat-like compound (5)
4 Petulant (5)
5 Regret with sadness (3)
7 State of armed conflict (3)
10 Hears (7)
12 Camera image (abbrev.) (5)
13 Mock (3)
14 Subatomic particle (5)
16 Intentionally so written (3)

No. 12
Wednesday January 12th 2022

Across

6 Freedom from dirt (11)
7 Religious acts (5)
9 Male parent (5)
10 Spacecraft that circles the planet (7)
13 Enrol (anag) (5)
14 Film with Will Smith as a matchmaker (5)
15 Very steep (11)

Down

1 Fruit of the oak (5)
2 Region including Cornwall and Devon (4,7)
3 Send off to a destination (8)
4 Reinstatement (11)
5 Russian sovereigns (5)
8 Residential district on the outskirts of a city (8)
11 Aromatic spice (5)
12 Stage (5)

No. 13
Thursday January 13th 2022

Across
1. Scanty (6)
4. Corrosive substance (4)
7. Extent (5)
8. Sky-blue colour (5)
9. Firmly (7)
11. Looked up to (7)
13. Main (5)
14. Let (5)
15. Volcano in Sicily (4)
16. A complex whole (6)

Down
1. Fashions; styles (5)
2. Name or title (11)
3. Eg drink lots of water after exercise (9)
5. Apron cutter (anag) (11)
6. Put clothes on (5)
8. Awfully (9)
10. Immature insects (5)
12. You usually do this whilst asleep (5)

No. 14
Friday January 14th 2022

Across
6. Freely (11)
7. ___ Willis: daughter of Demi Moore (5)
8. Annoy (5)
9. Cheep (7)
12. Long rods (5)
13. Edward ___ : composer (5)
14. Frivolous (5-6)

Down
1. Creamy-white colour (5)
2. Act gloomily (anag) (11)
3. Automatons (8)
4. Emergency service (4,7)
5. Computer memory units (5)
8. Pitiful (8)
10. What a wizard might cast (5)
11. Assess (5)

No. 15
Saturday January 15th 2022

Across

6 Remark; comment (11)
7 Not together (5)
9 Performed on stage (5)
10 Animal fat (7)
13 Of the nose (5)
14 Gate fastener (5)
15 Eg without a beard (5-6)

Down

1 This date (5)
2 Founded (11)
3 Similarity (8)
4 Noticeably different (11)
5 Dines (anag) (5)
8 Prickling sensation (8)
11 Bump into (5)
12 Solid piece of something (5)

No. 16
Sunday January 16th 2022

Across

1 Sent back to one's own country (11)
7 Matured (7)
8 Humming sound (5)
9 Form of oxygen (5)
12 Amide (anag) (5)
13 Musical note (5)
14 Gap in rocks (7)
16 Word meanings (11)

Down

1 Platform (7)
2 Penetrated (7)
3 Conclusion; ending (11)
4 A change for the better (11)
5 Unit of weight (3)
6 Broken equipment (3)
10 River in South America (7)
11 Foes (7)
14 Popular edible fish (3)
15 Creature with pointed ears (3)

No. 17
Monday January 17th 2022

Across

1 Feigned (9)
6 Country in East Asia (5)
7 Staple (5)
9 A long wandering journey (7)
12 Acts in a disloyal manner (7)
16 Heavy noble gas (5)
17 Froths (5)
18 Kept up (9)

Down

2 Amps (anag) (4)
3 Foreign language (informal) (5)
4 Domestic cat (5)
5 Discontinuance (6)
6 Music player (7)
8 Demureness (7)
10 24-hour period (3)
11 Makes amends for (6)
13 Female relatives (5)
14 Capital of Bulgaria (5)
15 First light (4)

No. 18
Tuesday January 18th 2022

Across

1 Considerable (11)
7 Due (7)
8 School of fish (5)
9 Coarse twilled cotton fabric (5)
11 Water-filled ditches around castles (5)
12 Part of (5)
13 Renaissance (7)
16 Expansion (11)

Down

1 Sap (anag) (3)
2 Remuneration (3)
3 Needleworker (11)
4 Incalculable (11)
5 Plant with bright flowers (7)
6 Symbolic objects (7)
9 Master of ceremonies (7)
10 Endanger (7)
14 Cereal grass (3)
15 Small shelter (3)

No. 19
Wednesday January 19th 2022

Across

1 Mob rule (10)
6 Lose one's footing (4)
7 Concealing (6)
8 Feel sorrow for one's deeds (6)
9 Stitches (4)
11 Run quickly (4)
13 Famous French museum (6)
15 Not awake (6)
17 Work hard (4)
18 At all (10)

Down

2 Volcanic crater (7)
3 Slight error; oversight (5)
4 Mountain range in South America (5)
5 Longing (3)
7 Head covering (3)
10 Period of conflict (7)
12 Doglike mammal (5)
13 Remove branches (3)
14 Unfasten (5)
16 Lay seed in the ground (3)

No. 20
Thursday January 20th 2022

Across

2 Of enormous effect (7)
6 Female sheep (pl.) (4)
9 Religious sister (3)
10 Ascended (7)
11 Obvious (4-7)
12 Praised highly (7)
13 Metal container; element (3)
14 Backbone; fortitude (4)
15 Most profound (7)

Down

1 Stood for (11)
3 Intoxicate (9)
4 One who knows your thoughts (4,6)
5 Link together (11)
7 Brilliance (10)
8 Sad (9)

No. 21
Friday January 21st 2022

Across
6 Ornithologist (11)
7 Group of sports players (5)
9 Bitterly pungent (5)
10 Illuminate (5,2)
13 Point in question (5)
14 Period between childhood and adulthood (5)
15 Mortification (11)

Down
1 Humiliate (5)
2 Causing difficulties (11)
3 Furtive (8)
4 Curative (11)
5 Networks of lines (5)
8 Obstinately (8)
11 Levy (5)
12 Deliberate; cogitate (5)

No. 22
Saturday January 22nd 2022

Across
1 Refreshing drink (6,5)
7 Enigmas (7)
8 Game fish (5)
9 Smooth transition (5)
11 Needing to be scratched (5)
12 Faint southern constellation (5)
13 Small apes (7)
16 Accomplishment (11)

Down
1 Blade for rowing a boat (3)
2 Help; assist (3)
3 Bird of prey (6,5)
4 Defensible (11)
5 Stupid (7)
6 Feeling of great happiness (7)
9 Endurance (7)
10 Decorate food (7)
14 Be in debt (3)
15 Ease into a chair (3)

No. 23
Sunday January 23rd 2022

Across
2 Using extravagant language (9)
7 Fish eggs (3)
8 Vanish (9)
9 Permeate (9)
10 Taking dishonestly (9)
11 Even though (2,5,2)
13 Cheek (slang) (3)
14 Seriously (9)

Down
1 Potential (11)
2 Item of furniture one sleeps on (3)
3 Get the wrong idea (11)
4 Act of making peace (11)
5 Sheet (anag) (5)
6 Accurate timer (11)
10 Show-off (5)
12 Small winged insect (3)

No. 24
Monday January 24th 2022

Across
1 Confused mixture (8)
6 Spin quickly (5)
7 Eg salmon and coral (5)
9 Having pains (4)
10 Do the dishes (4-2)
12 Start a fire (6)
14 Mischievous god in Norse mythology (4)
17 Take delight in (5)
18 Exploiting unfairly (5)
19 Making a deep resonant sound (8)

Down
2 Nationality of Oscar Wilde (5)
3 Sacred (4)
4 Be attractive (6)
5 Intuitive feeling (5)
6 Device that records the movements of someone (7)
8 Extremely wet (7)
11 Type of ski race (6)
13 Not at all (5)
15 Aromatic vegetable (5)
16 Opposite of empty (4)

No. 25
Tuesday January 25th 2022

Across

1 Express in other words (10)
5 Fruits of the palm (5)
7 Erased (5)
9 Obtain by coercion (6)
10 ___ out: very tired (4)
12 Particles around a comet (4)
13 Opposite of top (6)
16 Dog (5)
17 Hurts (5)
18 Harmful (10)

Down

1 Chaplain in the armed services (5)
2 Show-offs (6)
3 Argues (4)
4 Advocate (9)
6 Carved and painted post (5,4)
8 Loud noise (3)
11 Style of architecture (6)
12 Policeman (3)
14 Thin fogs (5)
15 Keep away from (4)

No. 26
Wednesday January 26th 2022

Across

2 Large household water container (7)
5 Spiritual nourishment (5)
6 Ask for (7)
7 Brown earth pigment (5)
10 Boldly (11)
12 Examined furtively (5)
13 Round building (7)
14 Positions in a hierarchy (5)
15 Compress (7)

Down

1 A person in general (7)
2 Jeer noisily at (7)
3 Sixty minutes (4)
4 Informed upon (8)
7 Without warning (8)
8 Contrast (7)
9 Allots (7)
11 Entice (4)

No. 27
Thursday January 27th 2022

Across

3 Open declaration of affirmation (6)
6 Cool and distant (5)
7 Tensing a muscle (7)
9 Asian pepper plant (5)
12 Act of freeing from blame (11)
14 Angry (5)
15 Shore birds (7)
17 Levies (5)
18 Barriers (6)

Down

1 Placed a bet (7)
2 Ballroom dance (7)
3 Wealth (9)
4 Sticky yellowish substance (3)
5 Connect (4)
8 Writers (9)
10 Eventually (7)
11 Opposite (7)
13 Musical staff sign (4)
16 Small truck (3)

No. 28
Friday January 28th 2022

Across

2 Hot-tasting condiment (7)
5 Latin American dance (5)
6 Eg use a towel after showering (3-4)
7 Become suddenly understandable (5)
10 Eg full stops and commas (11)
12 Hidden storage space (5)
13 Call the validity of a practice into question (7)
14 Display freely (5)
15 Arachnids (7)

Down

1 Very old (7)
2 Promotes commercially (7)
3 Periodic movement of the sea (4)
4 Condemn publicly (8)
7 Skippers (8)
8 Spring locks for doors (7)
9 Thick (7)
11 Peruse (4)

No. 29
Saturday January 29th 2022

Across
1 Barely (8)
6 Competes in a speed contest (5)
7 Male elephants (5)
9 Nobleman (4)
10 Outer parts of bread loaves (6)
12 Season after summer (6)
14 Spots (4)
17 Will (5)
18 Brilliant and clear (5)
19 Training college for the priesthood (8)

Down
2 Ride a bike (5)
3 Optimistic (4)
4 Remains of a fire (6)
5 Screams (5)
6 Revokes (7)
8 Stop temporarily (7)
11 Symbol or representation (6)
13 Melts (5)
15 Conceal (5)
16 Cooking appliance (4)

No. 30
Sunday January 30th 2022

Across
1 Engine part (10)
5 Sudden constriction (5)
7 Eyelashes (5)
9 Hankers after (6)
10 Aquatic vertebrate (4)
12 Torso (4)
13 Belonging to them (6)
16 Variety or kind (5)
17 Burdened (5)
18 Recognised (10)

Down
1 Easy (of a job) (5)
2 Japanese dress (6)
3 Access illegally (4)
4 Altered fraudulently (9)
6 Forsaken (9)
8 Exclamation of surprise (3)
11 Hot pepper (6)
12 Implore (3)
14 Church council (5)
15 ___-Jacques Rousseau: philosopher (4)

No. 31
Monday January 31st 2022

Across

6 Spookiness (11)
7 Eg covered with bricks (5)
9 Camel-like animal (5)
10 Italian dish (7)
13 Earlier (5)
14 Long-legged wading bird (5)
15 Act of checking the accuracy of an instrument (11)

Down

1 Unconditional love (5)
2 Having a folding roof (of a car) (11)
3 Breaks an agreement (8)
4 Very large city (11)
5 Customary (5)
8 Explain using words (8)
11 With speed (5)
12 Sinks (anag) (5)

No. 32
Tuesday February 1st 2022

Across

1 Cried (4)
3 Alter or move slightly (6)
7 Gets through merit (5)
9 Tennis stroke (5)
10 Ancient Egyptian ruler (7)
11 Set in motion; agitated (7)
13 Wander aimlessly (5)
14 Every 24 hours (5)
15 Teaser (anag) (6)
16 Unattractive (4)

Down

1 Cause (havoc) (5)
2 Type of artist (11)
4 Threw away (9)
5 Illogical (11)
6 Eg incisors and molars (5)
8 Very successful performer (9)
11 Move sideways (5)
12 Shyly (5)

No. 33
Wednesday February 2nd 2022

Across

1. Athletics event (6,4)
5. Regulations (5)
7. Ball of lead (5)
9. Smile affectedly (6)
10. Assist (4)
12. Speck (4)
13. A system of measurement (6)
16. Hymn of thanksgiving (5)
17. Conical tent (5)
18. Things that are necessary (10)

Down

1. Gets weary (5)
2. Endured (6)
3. Practical joke (4)
4. Device for catching rodents (9)
6. Boundless (9)
8. Bread roll (3)
11. Group of six (6)
12. Amp (anag) (3)
14. Board game (5)
15. Leg joint (4)

No. 34
Thursday February 3rd 2022

Across

2. Be too intense for (9)
7. Signal assent with the head (3)
8. Medical analysis (9)
9. Say clearly (9)
10. Month (9)
11. Depose (9)
13. Decay (3)
14. Harshness of tone (9)

Down

1. Unwilling to believe (11)
2. Eccentric; strange (3)
3. Freed (11)
4. Solid figure with five faces (11)
5. Use inefficiently; rubbish (5)
6. Eating establishments (11)
10. Absolute (5)
12. Dry and mocking (3)

No. 35
Friday February 4th 2022

Across

3 Delights greatly (6)
6 In a slow tempo (of music) (5)
7 Pasta strips (7)
9 Restore factory settings (5)
12 Small storage space (11)
14 Strange and mysterious (5)
15 Unite together (7)
17 Browned bread (5)
18 Abilities (6)

Down

1 Clergymen (7)
2 Annoying (7)
3 Lowest female singing voice (9)
4 Fishing pole (3)
5 Prophet (4)
8 Medicinal creams (9)
10 Gossip (7)
11 Swears (7)
13 Pool (anag) (4)
16 Chatter (3)

No. 36
Saturday February 5th 2022

Across

2 The North Star (7)
6 Tall cereal grass (4)
9 Mongrel dog (3)
10 Ancestry (7)
11 Remembered (11)
12 Living in water (7)
13 Argument against something (3)
14 Plant with an edible root (4)
15 Cause to taste more sugary (7)

Down

1 Happenings (11)
3 Tough connective bodily tissues (9)
4 Container (10)
5 Good fortune (11)
7 Unwillingness (10)
8 Fierce attack (9)

No. 37
Sunday February 6th 2022

Across
1 Permissible (9)
6 Bring on oneself (5)
7 Three-note chord (5)
9 Complex wholes (7)
12 Moves up and down repeatedly (7)
16 Decline sharply (5)
17 Severe (5)
18 World you visit when asleep (9)

Down
2 Good fortune (4)
3 Electrical cables (5)
4 Grips with the teeth (5)
5 US rapper (6)
6 Demands forcefully (7)
8 Merit (7)
10 Deviate off course (3)
11 Pay back money (6)
13 Plentiful (5)
14 Group of bees (5)
15 Country whose capital is Havana (4)

No. 38
Monday February 7th 2022

Across
6 Action of stealing from a store (11)
7 ___ Els: golfer (5)
8 Game similar to bowls (5)
9 Share; portion (7)
12 Unit of length (5)
13 Hang with cloth (5)
14 Self-centred (11)

Down
1 Anaemic-looking (5)
2 Suggested or implied idea (11)
3 Cause to feel isolated (8)
4 Inconsistency (11)
5 Leers (5)
8 Make valid retrospectively (8)
10 Implant (5)
11 Attractive young lady (5)

No. 39
Tuesday February 8th 2022

Across
1 Aircraft (pl.) (11)
8 Assumed proposition (5)
9 Difficult to catch (7)
10 Conventional (11)
13 The sun and stars (poetic) (7)
14 Feeling of boredom (5)
15 Unthinking (11)

Down
2 Small pit or cavity (6)
3 Controversial (9)
4 Deciduous trees (4)
5 Formless (9)
6 Will (9)
7 Completing (9)
11 Sewing instrument (6)
12 Knowledge (abbrev.) (4)

No. 40
Wednesday February 9th 2022

Across
2 Flaw (7)
6 Egg-shaped (4)
9 Atmospheric murk; obscure (3)
10 Stations at the ends of routes (7)
11 Device for measuring time (11)
12 Capital of Georgia in the US (7)
13 Bed for a baby (3)
14 Swollen mark (4)
15 Goals (7)

Down
1 State of the USA (11)
3 Kit; gear (9)
4 Gain access to gradually (10)
5 Prominent (4,7)
7 Dynamo (10)
8 Convert to another language (9)

No. 41
Thursday February 10th 2022

Across
1 Changeable (9)
5 Speak in a confused way (6)
7 Change (4)
8 Put to practical use (7)
11 Unintelligent (7)
14 Listen to (4)
15 Background actors (6)
16 Reduced (9)

Down
1 European country (7)
2 Kettledrums (7)
3 Floor of a building (5)
4 Soft cheese (4)
6 Cost (7)
9 Turns upside down (7)
10 Clad (7)
12 Pace (4)
13 The Norwegian language (5)

No. 42
Friday February 11th 2022

Across
1 Muttering angrily (8)
6 Slender piece of wood (5)
7 Buckets (5)
9 Inlets (4)
10 Valuable things; strengths (6)
12 Make something new (6)
14 ___ Macpherson: Australian model (4)
17 Eg from Athens (5)
18 High up (5)
19 Anxious uncertainty (8)

Down
2 Showery (5)
3 Became alert after sleep (4)
4 Enforce compliance with (6)
5 Craftiness (5)
6 Crying heavily (7)
8 Believe tentatively (7)
11 Eg adder and python (6)
13 Changes direction suddenly (5)
15 Big cats (5)
16 Sheet of paper in a book (4)

No. 43
Saturday February 12th 2022

Across

6 Record players (11)
7 Andrew Lloyd Webber musical (5)
8 In what place (5)
9 Person devoted to love (7)
12 Moves back and forth (5)
13 Sharp end (5)
14 Explained the meaning of (11)

Down

1 ___ Nash: writer of light verse (5)
2 Papal state (7,4)
3 Red fruits eaten as vegetables (8)
4 Doubt (11)
5 Cinders (5)
8 Speaks very quietly (8)
10 Daniel ___ : James Bond actor (5)
11 Examine (5)

No. 44
Sunday February 13th 2022

Across

1 Airport checking devices (8)
6 Stylishness and originality (5)
7 Standpoint (5)
9 ___ Simone: US singer (4)
10 Approached (6)
12 Pay attention to what is said (6)
14 Frozen precipitation (4)
17 Play a guitar (5)
18 Shaped up (5)
19 How a crab moves (8)

Down

2 Series of linked metal rings (5)
3 Geek (4)
4 Pencil rubber (6)
5 Sweetening substance (5)
6 Closing sections of compositions (7)
8 Given; bequeathed (7)
11 Appeared to be (6)
13 Rises (anag) (5)
15 Nursemaid (5)
16 Pack carefully and neatly (4)

No. 45
Monday February 14th 2022

Across
- **3** Quantity (6)
- **6** Balance (5)
- **7** Watching (7)
- **9** Thin pancake (5)
- **12** A recollection (11)
- **14** Rinse out (5)
- **15** Grim or dismal (7)
- **17** Thermosetting resin (5)
- **18** Rephrase (6)

Down
- **1** Connoisseur; gourmet (7)
- **2** Difficult choice (7)
- **3** At no time hereafter (9)
- **4** Knot with a double loop (3)
- **5** Peel (4)
- **8** Conveyed an opinion (9)
- **10** Sharp tooth (7)
- **11** Shows again (7)
- **13** Lion noise (4)
- **16** Opposite of high (3)

No. 46
Tuesday February 15th 2022

Across
- **1** Written copy (10)
- **5** What an author writes (5)
- **7** Manages (5)
- **9** Walked quickly (6)
- **10** 365 days (4)
- **12** Gardening tools used for weeding (4)
- **13** Inspirational people (6)
- **16** Metal worker (5)
- **17** Epic poem ascribed to Homer (5)
- **18** Amazes (10)

Down
- **1** Melodies (5)
- **2** Food that is not liquid (6)
- **3** Wealthy (4)
- **4** Spicy sausage (9)
- **6** Different versions of something (9)
- **8** A knight (3)
- **11** Third sign of the zodiac (6)
- **12** Belonging to him (3)
- **14** Teams (5)
- **15** Drive away (4)

No. 47
Wednesday February 16th 2022

Across

3 Public square in Italy (6)
6 Musical instrument (5)
7 Render utterly perplexed (7)
9 Timer (anag) (5)
12 In unbroken sequence (11)
14 Sufficiently (5)
15 Restrict (7)
17 Cloth woven from flax (5)
18 Sweet (6)

Down

1 Greed (7)
2 Secretion of an endocrine gland (7)
3 Belief that God is in all things (9)
4 Hit forcibly (3)
5 Touch (4)
8 As might be expected (9)
10 Tearing (7)
11 Declaring to be untrue (7)
13 Undergarments (4)
16 Cup (3)

No. 48
Thursday February 17th 2022

Across

1 Unpleasant (11)
7 Foot support (7)
8 Detailed assessment of accounts (5)
9 Eg copper or calcium (5)
12 Conjuring trick (5)
13 Governed (5)
14 Powdered spice (7)
16 Insanity (11)

Down

1 Early 20th century art movement (7)
2 Moving smoothly (7)
3 State of preoccupation (11)
4 Group of three (11)
5 Distant (3)
6 One circuit of a track (3)
10 Catchphrase (7)
11 Noisiest (7)
14 Collection of many sheets of paper (3)
15 Level golf score (3)

No. 49
Friday February 18th 2022

Across

1 Mechanic in the armed forces (9)
7 Long period of time (3)
8 Type of printer (3,6)
9 Grease (9)
10 Method of teaching a new language (9)
12 English actress in The Avengers (5,4)
13 Nay (anag) (3)
14 Limit; edge (9)

Down

1 Incorporating sound and images (11)
2 Absolute (5)
3 Astound (11)
4 Document confirming an achievement (11)
5 Tyrannosaurus ___ : dinosaur (3)
6 Unintentionally (11)
11 Makhaya ___ : South African cricketer (5)
12 Hair colourant (3)

No. 50
Saturday February 19th 2022

Across

1 Item of neckwear (6)
4 Move fast in a straight line (4)
7 Remove paint from a wall (5)
8 ___ Arabia: country (5)
9 Device that measures electric current (7)
11 Jumps up suddenly (7)
13 Fine powdery foodstuff (5)
14 From that time (5)
15 Cloth worn around the waist (4)
16 Organic compounds (6)

Down

1 ___ del Sol: region of Spain (5)
2 Bitter; angry (of speech) (11)
3 Small dish eaten before a meal (9)
5 Visage (11)
6 God (5)
8 Shocks (9)
10 Presents (5)
12 Gardeners sow these (5)

No. 51
Sunday February 20th 2022

Across

- **2** Lie (7)
- **6** Where one finds Tehran (4)
- **9** Gave a meal to (3)
- **10** Trailblazer (7)
- **11** Thoroughly tidy the house (6,5)
- **12** Collection of sheets of paper (7)
- **13** Deep hole in the ground (3)
- **14** Variety; sort (4)
- **15** Maxims (7)

Down

- **1** Magnifying instruments (11)
- **3** Stargazing instrument (9)
- **4** Hostile (10)
- **5** Children's game (4-3-4)
- **7** Seemingly (10)
- **8** Perception (9)

No. 52
Monday February 21st 2022

Across

- **1** Casual (10)
- **5** Porcelain (5)
- **7** Recommended strongly (5)
- **9** Revolve (6)
- **10** Remnant (4)
- **12** Configuration; shape (4)
- **13** Constructs (6)
- **16** Woody tissue (5)
- **17** Published false statement (5)
- **18** Children's carer (10)

Down

- **1** More pleasant (5)
- **2** Card game similar to whist (6)
- **3** Noisy (4)
- **4** Disco (9)
- **6** Among other things (Latin) (5,4)
- **8** Give a nickname to (3)
- **11** Central parts of cells (6)
- **12** Mammal with a bushy tail (3)
- **14** Pertaining to the sun (5)
- **15** Prestigious TV award (4)

29

No. 53
Tuesday February 22nd 2022

Across
1 Plan of action (6)
4 Moved through water (4)
7 Amounts of medication (5)
8 Singing voices (5)
9 Inactive (7)
11 Certificate (7)
13 Culinary herb (5)
14 Piece of information (5)
15 Ascend (4)
16 Sprightliness (6)

Down
1 ___ with: supported (5)
2 Theatrical behaviour (11)
3 Maltreat (9)
5 Shaman (5,6)
6 Ponders (5)
8 The direct opposite of a thing (9)
10 Coder (anag) (5)
12 Confess to (5)

No. 54
Wednesday February 23rd 2022

Across
1 Flower (6-2-3)
7 Country in West Africa (7)
8 Sticky sweet liquid (5)
9 Tree branch (5)
11 Modifies (5)
12 Softly radiant (5)
13 Sterile (7)
16 Happiness (11)

Down
1 Cooling tool (3)
2 Piece of cloth (3)
3 Clay pottery (11)
4 Quantification (11)
5 Capital of Kenya (7)
6 Moderates; mitigates (7)
9 Pertaining to plants (7)
10 Insanitary (7)
14 Definite article (3)
15 Feline (3)

No. 55
Thursday February 24th 2022

Across

1 Of the highest quality (5-5)
5 Small streams (5)
7 City in Tuscany (5)
9 Last light (6)
10 Prima donna (4)
12 Princess ___ : Star Wars character (4)
13 Word that qualifies another (6)
16 Show off (5)
17 Bundle of wheat (5)
18 Dividing into parts (10)

Down

1 Internal parasites (5)
2 Removed dirt from (6)
3 Hang loosely; droop (4)
4 Violation of anything sacred (9)
6 Angular distance east or west (9)
8 Shola ___ : singer (3)
11 Thomas ___ : US inventor (6)
12 ___ Tyler: US actress (3)
14 Confuse or obscure (5)
15 Plant stalk (4)

No. 56
Friday February 25th 2022

Across

2 Shocking surprise (9)
7 Frozen water (3)
8 Relaxed and not highly strung (4-5)
9 Eg dynamite (9)
10 Chew (9)
11 Cascade (9)
13 Organ of sight (3)
14 Thought deeply about (9)

Down

1 Landmark in Paris (6,5)
2 Insect that can sting (3)
3 Misinterpret (11)
4 Important (11)
5 Expulsion (5)
6 Dizzy (5-6)
10 Distinctive design (5)
12 Was in first place (3)

No. 57
Saturday February 26th 2022

Across
1 Act of changing sides (9)
7 Beer (3)
8 Arthur ___ : British astrophysicist (9)
9 Parted (9)
10 Meddlesome (9)
12 Deviating from what is standard (9)
13 Cut of pork (3)
14 24 hours ago (9)

Down
1 Battleship (11)
2 Loses colour (5)
3 Easily seen (11)
4 Put questions to (11)
5 Grandmother (3)
6 Tunefully (11)
11 Pointed weapon (5)
12 ___ Winehouse: singer (3)

No. 58
Sunday February 27th 2022

Across
1 Depth of knowledge (10)
6 Level and regular (4)
7 Fastening devices (6)
8 Contemptibly small (6)
9 Melt (4)
11 Inclined plane (4)
13 Far away (6)
15 What a spider makes (6)
17 Dispatched (4)
18 Island in the Indian Ocean (10)

Down
2 Mediterranean coastal region (7)
3 Pays for financially (5)
4 Not suitable (5)
5 Pay (anag) (3)
7 Shed tears (3)
10 Aerial (7)
12 Scraped at (5)
13 Steal (3)
14 Hides (5)
16 Unit of resistance (3)

No. 59
Monday February 28th 2022

Across

1 Region of France (6)
4 Dutch cheese (4)
7 Nobleman (5)
8 Sleeveless cloaks (5)
9 Process of setting something in motion (5-2)
11 Unfasten (7)
13 Edgar ___ : French artist (5)
14 Garbage or drivel (5)
15 Slanting; crooked (4)
16 Wears down (6)

Down

1 ___ Dumbledore: Harry Potter character (5)
2 Stretch out completely (11)
3 Interprets in a certain way (9)
5 Poverty (11)
6 Untidy (5)
8 Electrical component (9)
10 Travels on a bicycle (5)
12 Looks furtively (5)

No. 60
Tuesday March 1st 2022

Across

1 Set out on a voyage (8)
6 Assisted (5)
7 Make available for sale (5)
9 Protest march (abbrev.) (4)
10 Consisting of flowers (6)
12 Plan; strategy (6)
14 Eager (4)
17 Insurgent (5)
18 Long poems (5)
19 Separate and distinct (8)

Down

2 Device used to connect to the internet (5)
3 Helps (4)
4 Small hills (6)
5 Postpone (5)
6 Accounts inspector (7)
8 Becomes less severe (7)
11 Holds and uses a tool (6)
13 Raised to the third power (5)
15 Kick out (5)
16 Hind part (4)

No. 61
Wednesday March 2nd 2022

Across

1 Sensible (9)
6 Supply with food (5)
7 Requirements (5)
9 Yelled with excitement (7)
12 Waterfall (7)
16 Seventh sign of the zodiac (5)
17 Slopes (5)
18 Massive land mammals (9)

Down

2 Block a decision (4)
3 Drinking tube (5)
4 Stringed instrument (5)
5 Absolve (6)
6 Part of a church near the altar (7)
8 Sorrow (7)
10 Removed from sight (3)
11 Functional (6)
13 Decrease; lessen (5)
14 Our planet (5)
15 Augury (4)

No. 62
Thursday March 3rd 2022

Across

1 Within one's financial means (10)
6 Worry about (4)
7 Eccentricity (6)
8 Steal livestock (6)
9 Created (4)
11 Animal's den (4)
13 Large marine mammals (6)
15 River in South America (6)
17 Woes; problems (4)
18 Bored with life (5-5)

Down

2 Prescription (7)
3 Group of eight (5)
4 Darken (5)
5 Consume food (3)
7 Single in number (3)
10 Inhabitant (7)
12 Sharp blade (5)
13 Finish first (3)
14 Not dead (5)
16 Cry of a cat or gull (3)

No. 63
Friday March 4th 2022

Across

1 Jobs (11)
8 Take the place of (5)
9 Dispute or competition (7)
10 Unnecessary (11)
13 Make less heavy (7)
14 Fruit of the vine (5)
15 Divisor (11)

Down

2 Doze (6)
3 Necessarily true statement (9)
4 Musical composition (4)
5 Speculating (9)
6 Eg floods and earthquakes (4,2,3)
7 Fossil fuel (9)
11 Deceive with ingenuity (6)
12 Liquid precipitation (4)

No. 64
Saturday March 5th 2022

Across

1 Laugh boisterously (6)
4 First man (4)
7 Small lakes (5)
8 Locates or places (5)
9 Panting (7)
11 Flowering shrubs (7)
13 Perfume (5)
14 Favouring extreme views (5)
15 ___ Daly: TV presenter (4)
16 Well-being (6)

Down

1 Rise to one's feet (3,2)
2 Ancestors (11)
3 Attacker (9)
5 Harmful (11)
6 Hebrew prophet (5)
8 Autograph (9)
10 Tines (anag) (5)
12 Reduce prices substantially (5)

No. 65
Sunday March 6th 2022

Across

6 Controversial (11)
7 Eg petrol and coal (5)
8 Headdress worn by a bishop (5)
9 Process of wearing away (7)
12 Sea crew member (5)
13 Gastropod with a shell (5)
14 Spongy item of confectionery (11)

Down

1 Mark or wear thin (5)
2 Needless (11)
3 Cutlery used to stir a drink (8)
4 All the time (11)
5 Trembling poplar (5)
8 Cornerstone (8)
10 Barack ___ : 44th US President (5)
11 Reduces one's speed (5)

No. 66
Monday March 7th 2022

Across

3 Situation that appears irresolvable (6)
6 Very masculine (5)
7 Arranged neatly (7)
9 Upright (5)
12 Not wanted (11)
14 Reside (5)
15 Gather (7)
17 Incision; indent (5)
18 Freshest (6)

Down

1 Momentum (7)
2 Long speeches (7)
3 Revolting (9)
4 Pitcher (3)
5 Look or manner (4)
8 Rash (9)
10 Opposes (7)
11 Affluent (7)
13 Device sounding a warning (4)
16 Solemn pledge (3)

No. 67
Tuesday March 8th 2022

Across

6 Irritable (3-8)
7 Wound from a wasp (5)
9 Door hanger (5)
10 Not physically existing (7)
13 Herb (5)
14 Colossus (5)
15 Daring (11)

Down

1 Wash with clean water (5)
2 Person who foresees the future (11)
3 Force lifting something up (8)
4 Act of moving from one place to another (11)
5 Lazes; does nothing (5)
8 Beautiful (8)
11 Heating apparatus (5)
12 Attach to (5)

No. 68
Wednesday March 9th 2022

Across

1 King Arthur's legendary sword (9)
6 One who puts in a lot of effort (5)
7 Leaps (5)
9 Sped along; skimmed (7)
12 Chaps (7)
16 Ascend (5)
17 Exposes secret information (5)
18 Assembly (9)

Down

2 Protruding part of the lower jaw (4)
3 Lingers furtively (5)
4 Small and elegant (5)
5 Put right (6)
6 Trade in something illegal (7)
8 Attracts powerfully (7)
10 Domestic bovine animal (3)
11 Working steadily with a tool (6)
13 Circle a planet (5)
14 Find an answer to (5)
15 Where one finds Bamako (4)

No. 69
Thursday March 10th 2022

Across
6 Disturb the status quo (4,3,4)
7 Thin mortar (5)
9 Very untypical (5)
10 Bouncer (7)
13 Below zero (of temperature) (5)
14 Small spot (5)
15 Everything that orbits the sun (5,6)

Down
1 Sediment (5)
2 Consequently (11)
3 Pleasant scents (8)
4 Administrations (11)
5 Tend a fire (5)
8 Clothing that covers the legs (8)
11 Wrong (5)
12 Economise (5)

No. 70
Friday March 11th 2022

Across
6 Pleasant to think about but unrealistic (3,2,3,3)
7 Contest (5)
8 Stood up (5)
9 Guglielmo ___ : radio pioneer (7)
12 Covered the inside of a bin (5)
13 Trite (anag) (5)
14 Estates where crops are grown on a large scale (11)

Down
1 Foam or froth (5)
2 Letter of recommendation (11)
3 Moored (8)
4 Affiliation (11)
5 Uses a keyboard (5)
8 Religious deserter (8)
10 Applauds (5)
11 Nationality of Tom Jones (5)

No. 71
Saturday March 12th 2022

Across

1 Fast-flying insects (11)
8 Measuring stick (5)
9 Reinstate (7)
10 Not held up (11)
13 Unfamiliar (7)
14 Tall structure on a castle (5)
15 Incidental expense (11)

Down

2 Comes up (6)
3 Pyrotechnics (9)
4 Lazy (4)
5 Dispersing (9)
6 Emotionally disturbing (9)
7 Medley of dried petals (9)
11 Inhabitant of Troy (6)
12 White aquatic bird (4)

No. 72
Sunday March 13th 2022

Across

1 Commercial (10)
5 Card game (5)
7 Taut (5)
9 Disdains (6)
10 Implement for styling hair (4)
12 Lean (4)
13 Type of market (6)
16 Ye old (anag) (5)
17 Stratum (5)
18 One who gives to a cause (10)

Down

1 Sulks (5)
2 Exposing one's views (6)
3 Young children (4)
4 Roman foot soldier (9)
6 General erudition (9)
8 Bath vessel (3)
11 Flowering plant (6)
12 Attempt to do (3)
14 Less common (5)
15 Adhesive (4)

No. 73
Monday March 14th 2022

Across

1 Syllabus (10)
6 Stock of money (4)
7 Indistinct (6)
8 Be owned by (6)
9 Bent wire for hanging things on (4)
11 Insects that make honey (4)
13 Highest point (6)
15 Support (6)
17 Adds (4)
18 Unnecessarily (10)

Down

2 Four-stringed guitar (7)
3 Cowboy exhibition (5)
4 Giggle (5)
5 Russian space station (3)
7 Listening device (3)
10 Most favourable (7)
12 Portion of a play (5)
13 Part of a coat (3)
14 Birds lay their eggs in these (5)
16 Criticise strongly (3)

No. 74
Tuesday March 15th 2022

Across

1 Bitterness of manner (8)
6 Bronze medal position (5)
7 Prize (5)
9 Nourishment (4)
10 Scuffle (6)
12 Without difficulty (6)
14 One of the continents (4)
17 Major artery (5)
18 Dark wood (5)
19 Unreliable; shifty (8)

Down

2 Capital of Egypt (5)
3 Repeat (4)
4 Son of Daedalus in Greek mythology (6)
5 Periods of 12 months (5)
6 Silklike fabric (7)
8 Relating to what you eat (7)
11 Opposite of an acid (6)
13 Indian garments (5)
15 Track of an animal (5)
16 Less than average tide (4)

No. 75
Wednesday March 16th 2022

Across
1 Switched off (11)
8 Cuts slightly (5)
9 Changed gradually over time (7)
10 Obstacle; barrier (11)
13 Active part of a fire (7)
14 Similar (5)
15 Make room for (11)

Down
2 Protective kitchen garments (6)
3 Clear of blame (9)
4 Thoughtfulness (4)
5 Appoint to an office (9)
6 Sensational dramatic work (9)
7 Be too strong for (9)
11 African antelope (6)
12 Metallic element (4)

No. 76
Thursday March 17th 2022

Across
2 Arid areas (7)
6 Depend upon (4)
9 Layer of a folded material (3)
10 Broad knife (7)
11 An argument that does not follow (3,8)
12 Distant runner-up in a horse race (4-3)
13 Sphere or globe (3)
14 Rip up (4)
15 Breastbone (7)

Down
1 Showy (11)
3 Protect from harm (9)
4 Feeling of deep sorrow (10)
5 Very tall buildings (11)
7 Deplorably bad (10)
8 Attainment of a position (9)

No. 77
Friday March 18th 2022

Across
- **2** Fast food item (9)
- **7** Before the present (3)
- **8** Places carefully (9)
- **9** Becomes larger (9)
- **10** Distribute (9)
- **11** Group of musicians (9)
- **13** Adult males (3)
- **14** Vehicle for interstellar travel (9)

Down
- **1** Meat-eating (11)
- **2** Leap on one foot (3)
- **3** An example of great artistry (11)
- **4** Satisfactory (2,2,7)
- **5** Surface shine (5)
- **6** Radiant; sumptuous (11)
- **10** Capital of Ghana (5)
- **12** Unit of current (3)

No. 78
Saturday March 19th 2022

Across
- **2** Accumulated over time (7)
- **6** Rodents (4)
- **9** Make less bright (3)
- **10** Unsurpassed (3-4)
- **11** Likeness (11)
- **12** Spanish beverage (7)
- **13** What painters create (3)
- **14** Opposite of thick (4)
- **15** Creepiest (7)

Down
- **1** Act evasively (11)
- **3** Minute blood vessel (9)
- **4** Below (10)
- **5** Very controlling (11)
- **7** Semiconductor device (10)
- **8** Eradicate (9)

No. 79
Sunday March 20th 2022

Across
3 Strongbox for valuables (6)
6 Plantain lily (5)
7 Servile (7)
9 Ousel (anag) (5)
12 Give your full attention to (11)
14 Technical problem (5)
15 Trap for the unwary (7)
17 Later (5)
18 Appearing larger (of the moon) (6)

Down
1 Cup (7)
2 Distributing (7)
3 Type of restaurant (9)
4 Wetland (3)
5 Step on a ladder (4)
8 Symbol of surrender (5,4)
10 Empty-headedness (7)
11 Warming devices (7)
13 Vista (4)
16 Facsimile (abbrev.) (3)

No. 80
Monday March 21st 2022

Across
2 Grotesque monster (7)
6 Electrically charged particles (4)
9 For each (3)
10 Not subject to a levy (3-4)
11 Constant (11)
12 Tall stand used by a preacher (7)
13 Pop music performance (3)
14 Adolescent (abbrev.) (4)
15 Perceive with the senses (7)

Down
1 Deterred (11)
3 Encroaches on (9)
4 Undergo; be faced with (10)
5 Rent manager (anag) (11)
7 Fossil fuel mostly made of methane (7,3)
8 Elaborate (9)

No. 81
Tuesday March 22nd 2022

Across

2 Young chicken (7)
5 Money (5)
6 Imperfections (7)
7 Lesser (5)
10 Free from financial concern (11)
12 Quartzlike gems (5)
13 Country in Africa (7)
14 Narrow roads (5)
15 Central cell part (7)

Down

1 Efficiency (7)
2 Where you sleep (7)
3 Dice (anag) (4)
4 Uneasy (8)
7 Soft leather shoe (8)
8 Walks leisurely (7)
9 Acquires (7)
11 Close securely; aquatic mammal (4)

No. 82
Wednesday March 23rd 2022

Across

1 Official (11)
8 Country in the Middle East (5)
9 Part of a chair (7)
10 Highest peak in Africa (11)
13 Quibble (7)
14 Move to music (5)
15 Nimble; fast (5-6)

Down

2 Standard; usual (6)
3 Stubborn (9)
4 Askew (4)
5 Annual compendiums of facts (9)
6 Reverse one's opinion (4-5)
7 Everlasting (9)
11 Among (6)
12 Obstacle (4)

No. 83
Thursday March 24th 2022

Across

2 Skill (7)
6 Unfortunately (4)
9 Knock vigorously (3)
10 Birthplace of Napoleon (7)
11 Ending that leaves one in suspense (11)
12 Beginning to exist (7)
13 Excellent serve (3)
14 Toon (anag) (4)
15 Tympanic membrane (7)

Down

1 Take part in (11)
3 Proposes a candidate for office (9)
4 Uncurl (10)
5 Detailed examination (11)
7 Person conducting a sale of lots (10)
8 University academic (9)

No. 84
Friday March 25th 2022

Across

1 A vain hope (4,5)
6 Country in East Africa (5)
7 Bequeath an income to (5)
9 Extremely bad (7)
12 Release (7)
16 Lively (5)
17 Very loud (5)
18 Halted temporarily (9)

Down

2 Evergreen coniferous tree (4)
3 Stage play (5)
4 Mournful poem (5)
5 Title used for a French woman (6)
6 Communal settlement in Israel (7)
8 Marsupial (7)
10 Form of public transport (3)
11 Sculptured symbols (6)
13 Chasm (5)
14 Therefore (5)
15 Intellectual faculty (4)

No. 85
Saturday March 26th 2022

Across
1 Biologist studying the environment (9)
5 Capital of Canada (6)
7 Earth's satellite (4)
8 Make insane (7)
11 Dark pigment in skin (7)
14 Part of a pedestal (4)
15 Deciduous flowering shrub (6)
16 Day of the week (9)

Down
1 Fact of being overly absorbed in oneself (7)
2 Relating to sight (7)
3 Brazilian dance (5)
4 Opposite of short (4)
6 United States (7)
9 Took small bites out of (7)
10 The growth of crystals (7)
12 Feeling of strong eagerness (4)
13 Isolated (5)

No. 86
Sunday March 27th 2022

Across
1 Container for waste (7,3)
5 Foot-operated lever (5)
7 Survived (5)
9 Repudiate (6)
10 Paul ___ : former England football captain (4)
12 Extras (cricket) (4)
13 Thespians (6)
16 Long for (5)
17 Penny-pincher (5)
18 Sleepiness (10)

Down
1 Swift (5)
2 Relations by marriage (2-4)
3 Strong and healthy (4)
4 People who create new products (9)
6 Poor condition (9)
8 Small numbered cube (3)
11 Norway lobsters (6)
12 Broad inlet of the sea (3)
14 Puts in order (5)
15 Understand (4)

No. 87
Monday March 28th 2022

Across

2 Conquered; was victorious (9)
7 Evergreen coniferous tree (3)
8 Contributions (9)
9 Extremely funny (9)
10 Tiresome (9)
11 Stubbornness (9)
13 Female sheep (3)
14 Strict and exacting (9)

Down

1 Occurring at the same time (11)
2 One more than one (3)
3 Data (11)
4 Person who looks identical to another (6,5)
5 Clock pointers (5)
6 Discontented (11)
10 Smarter (5)
12 Nevertheless (3)

No. 88
Tuesday March 29th 2022

Across

1 Foresee (10)
5 Law court official (5)
7 Funny person (5)
9 Expels (6)
10 Moved quickly (4)
12 Young horse (4)
13 Abdominal organ (6)
16 Tortilla topped with cheese (5)
17 Make a physical or mental effort (5)
18 Percussion instruments (10)

Down

1 Entertain (5)
2 Insertion marks (6)
3 Mischievous sprite (4)
4 Watch (9)
6 Pecking order (9)
8 Partly digested animal food (3)
11 Spoken address (6)
12 Enjoyable (3)
14 Short letters (5)
15 Neither good nor bad (2-2)

No. 89
Wednesday March 30th 2022

Across

1 Curved piece of wood (9)
6 Bamboo-eating animal (5)
7 Small woody plant (5)
9 Long pins (7)
12 Actually; in reality (2,5)
16 Belief in a creator (5)
17 Type of confection (5)
18 Young racehorses (9)

Down

2 Sound of a pig (4)
3 Tests (5)
4 Passage between rows of seats (5)
5 Narrow valleys (6)
6 Hit hard and often (7)
8 Made to individual order (7)
10 Clothing needed for an activity (3)
11 Representation of a person (6)
13 Punctuation mark (5)
14 Bits of meat of low value (5)
15 Biblical garden (4)

No. 90
Thursday March 31st 2022

Across

6 Air sport (4-7)
7 ___ firma: dry land (5)
8 English racecourse (5)
9 Medians (anag) (7)
12 Silk dress fabric (5)
13 ___ acid: protein building block (5)
14 Gymnastic devices (11)

Down

1 Colour of snow (5)
2 Increasing gradually by degrees (11)
3 Rural (8)
4 Debates (11)
5 Hard chalcedony (5)
8 Open to suggestion (8)
10 Makes a garment from wool (5)
11 Inferior to (5)

No. 91
Friday April 1st 2022

Across
1 Lower in value (6)
4 Suggestion; thought (4)
7 Pulpy (5)
8 Defence of the ___ : David Drury movie (5)
9 Tensing (anag) (7)
11 Impetuous person (7)
13 Prickly (5)
14 Small fruit used for oil (5)
15 Therefore (Latin) (4)
16 Judge (6)

Down
1 Evil spirit (5)
2 Very successful (of a book) (4-7)
3 Elegantly (9)
5 Set a limit on (4,3,4)
6 Targeted (5)
8 Morally justifiable (9)
10 Sense experience (5)
12 Judges (5)

No. 92
Saturday April 2nd 2022

Across
2 Getting bigger (7)
5 Roman country house (5)
6 Eg from Moscow (7)
7 Clergyman (5)
10 One in charge of a school (4,7)
12 Short and stout (5)
13 Endless (7)
14 Makes (a sound) (5)
15 Punched (7)

Down
1 Icy (7)
2 Attic rooms (7)
3 Cleanse (4)
4 Warily (8)
7 Fierce (8)
8 Wasted time (7)
9 Soft suede leather (7)
11 Harsh and miserable (4)

No. 93
Sunday April 3rd 2022

Across
3 Bloodsucking insect (6)
6 Public square (5)
7 Fixing; manipulating (7)
9 Alcoholic beverage (5)
12 Hinged; segmented (11)
14 Spear (5)
15 Armed conflict (7)
17 Watched secretly (5)
18 Sayings (6)

Down
1 Exceptionally good (7)
2 Outlaws (7)
3 Voracious marine fish (9)
4 Flexible container (3)
5 Mob (4)
8 Innocent (9)
10 Template (7)
11 Additions to a document (7)
13 Inner surface of the hand (4)
16 Mend (3)

No. 94
Monday April 4th 2022

Across
1 Small gulls (10)
5 Gestured at (5)
7 Deprive of weapons (5)
9 Kept private; unknown by others (6)
10 Remain (4)
12 Greasy (4)
13 Cuts off (6)
16 Moves its wings (of a bird) (5)
17 Cleanse the body (5)
18 Suppression of objectionable material (10)

Down
1 Flightless birds (5)
2 In truth; really (6)
3 Chemical salt used in dyeing (4)
4 Law that is passed (9)
6 Waver (9)
8 Month of the year (3)
11 One who belongs to a group (6)
12 Clumsy person (3)
14 A woolly ruminant animal (5)
15 Small vipers (4)

No. 95
Tuesday April 5th 2022

Across
6 Two missed serves in a row (tennis) (6,5)
7 Tablets (5)
8 Anaesthetic (5)
9 Novice driver (7)
12 Stomach (informal) (5)
13 Name of a book (5)
14 Tendency to disintegrate (11)

Down
1 Select; formally approve (5)
2 Capital of Malaysia (5,6)
3 Alphabetical list of terms (8)
4 Official bodies (11)
5 These shine at night (5)
8 Albert ___ : famous physicist (8)
10 Unable to move (5)
11 Hermann ___ : author of Steppenwolf (5)

No. 96
Wednesday April 6th 2022

Across
1 Elaborate; excessive (11)
7 Pursuing (7)
8 Christmas song (5)
9 Show indifference with the shoulders (5)
12 Small room used as a steam bath (5)
13 George ___ : Middlemarch writer (5)
14 Stomachs (7)
16 Briefly (11)

Down
1 Draws forth (7)
2 Henry David ___ : US author and poet (7)
3 Enthusiastic approval (11)
4 Insensitivity to pain (11)
5 ___ Titmuss: TV personality (3)
6 Pull at (3)
10 Pasta pockets (7)
11 Please or delight (7)
14 ___ Thumb: folklore character (3)
15 Mother (3)

No. 97
Thursday April 7th 2022

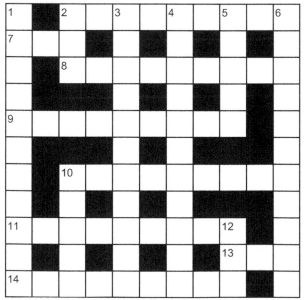

Across

2 Respects (7)
5 Showered with love (5)
6 Mournful (7)
7 Person who eats in a restaurant (5)
10 Accredited diplomats (11)
12 Moods (anag) (5)
13 Form of an element (7)
14 Eg performs karaoke (5)
15 Bewitch (7)

Down

1 Substitute (7)
2 Speech; where you live (7)
3 Wild mountain goat (4)
4 Musicians who perform alone (8)
7 Time by which a task must be completed (8)
8 Most difficult (7)
9 Large German city (7)
11 Skin irritation (4)

No. 98
Friday April 8th 2022

Across

2 Country in Central America (9)
7 Be nosy (3)
8 Movement from one place to another (9)
9 Variety of peach (9)
10 Personality (9)
11 Studying carefully (9)
13 Slip up (3)
14 Careful work or effort (9)

Down

1 Capital of Illinois (11)
2 Athletic facility (3)
3 Frustrating (11)
4 Evaluation (11)
5 Apart from (5)
6 Yearly celebration (11)
10 Move on hands and knees (5)
12 Command to a horse (3)

No. 99
Saturday April 9th 2022

Across

1 Prescience (9)
6 Flow with a whirling motion (5)
7 Ice cream is often served in these (5)
9 Expression of sorrow (7)
12 Rides at speed (7)
16 Tumble from a horse (5)
17 Escape from (5)
18 Supplant (9)

Down

2 Complain bitterly (4)
3 Latin American dance (5)
4 Type of lizard (5)
5 Connective tissue (6)
6 Smears (7)
8 Visible horizon (7)
10 Seed of an apple (3)
11 Spinal (anag) (6)
13 Spring flower (5)
14 Guide a vehicle (5)
15 Nobleman (4)

No. 100
Sunday April 10th 2022

Across

1 Severity of manner (9)
5 Reduce to a lower grade (6)
7 Slippery fish (pl.) (4)
8 Person who gives up (7)
11 Meatier (anag) (7)
14 Leave out (4)
15 Violent gust of wind (6)
16 Baffling stories (9)

Down

1 Moderately slow tempo (music) (7)
2 Japanese warriors (7)
3 Act of stealing (5)
4 Smoke passage (4)
6 Agrees or corresponds (7)
9 Huge wave (7)
10 Outcomes (7)
12 Communicate through gestures (4)
13 Hear a court case anew (5)

No. 101
Monday April 11th 2022

Across

1 Mixes together (6)
4 Race (anag) (4)
7 Large bags (5)
8 Moisten meat (5)
9 Non-professional (7)
11 An order to appear before a judge (7)
13 Town ___ : official who makes public announcements (5)
14 Hackneyed (5)
15 Without (literary) (4)
16 Speaks publicly (6)

Down

1 ___ Rhymes: rapper (5)
2 Sudden cry expressing surprise (11)
3 Cash ___ : ATM machine (9)
5 Astronomer who studies the origin of the universe (11)
6 Coarse rock used for polishing (5)
8 Device that measures air pressure (9)
10 Shoe ties (5)
12 Plant stalks (5)

No. 102
Tuesday April 12th 2022

Across

2 Clustered together (7)
5 A leaf of paper (5)
6 Uncovers (7)
7 Church singers (5)
10 Images recorded on film (11)
12 Small loose stones (5)
13 Brave (7)
14 Abatement (5)
15 Release from captivity (3,4)

Down

1 Intoxicating element in wine (7)
2 Kind of whisky (7)
3 Natter (4)
4 Mild aversion (8)
7 Hostages (8)
8 Grapple with (7)
9 Direct or control (7)
11 Vex (4)

No. 103
Wednesday April 13th 2022

Across

1 Demeaning (9)
5 Banner or flag (6)
7 Dell (4)
8 Comparison (7)
11 Upward slopes (7)
14 Molten rock (4)
15 Outer part of a bird's wing (6)
16 Made reference to (9)

Down

1 Part of the ocean (4,3)
2 Of the stomach (7)
3 Pertaining to warships (5)
4 Stop up a hole (4)
6 Without interruption (3-4)
9 Enthusiastic reception (7)
10 Longed for (7)
12 Pierce with a knife (4)
13 Fill with high spirits (5)

No. 104
Thursday April 14th 2022

Across

6 Inventiveness (11)
7 Walked up and down (5)
8 Pellucid (5)
9 ___ power: energy source (7)
12 Ways or tracks (5)
13 Parrot (5)
14 Ornaments worn by a monarch at coronation (5,6)

Down

1 Chilly (5)
2 Captivation (11)
3 Bridge-like structures (8)
4 Banger (11)
5 Breathe heavily at night (5)
8 Light afternoon meal (5,3)
10 Piquant (5)
11 Covered with water (5)

No. 105
Friday April 15th 2022

Across

1 Very charming (11)
7 Periodical (7)
8 Word of farewell (5)
9 Pipes (5)
12 ___ Camera: band (5)
13 A central point (5)
14 Sanction (7)
16 Distinguished (11)

Down

1 Variety of rummy (7)
2 Juicy soft fruit (7)
3 Unwise (11)
4 Climber (11)
5 Large cask (3)
6 Mountain pass (3)
10 Boastful behaviour (7)
11 Abandons a plan (7)
14 ___ MacGraw: Love Story star (3)
15 Friend (3)

No. 106
Saturday April 16th 2022

Across

1 At first (10)
6 Church recess (4)
7 Large wine bottle (6)
8 Mix socially (6)
9 Final (4)
11 Snares; bags (4)
13 Units of linear measure (6)
15 Pay no attention to (6)
17 Not difficult (4)
18 Process of dealing with people (10)

Down

2 Reprimand (7)
3 Obtain information from various sources (5)
4 Allowed by official rules (5)
5 Not me (3)
7 Gang (3)
10 Cowboy hat (7)
12 Open disrespect (5)
13 Anger (3)
14 Dairy product (5)
16 Chewy substance (3)

No. 107
Sunday April 17th 2022

Across
1 Acting out a part (4,7)
7 Largest (7)
8 Authoritative proclamation (5)
9 Acer tree (5)
11 Mix up or confuse (5)
12 Makes less dense (5)
13 Fragment (7)
16 Wrongly (11)

Down
1 Mock (3)
2 Fall behind (3)
3 One who held a job previously (11)
4 Another option (11)
5 Asked to come along (7)
6 Movement conveying an expression (7)
9 Type of cocktail (7)
10 Large ocean (7)
14 Tap (anag) (3)
15 Your (poetic) (3)

No. 108
Monday April 18th 2022

Across
6 Ecclesiastical jurisdiction (11)
7 Partly melted snow (5)
9 Leads (anag) (5)
10 Able to pay one's debts (7)
13 Liquid essential for life (5)
14 Rapidity of movement (5)
15 Troop leader (11)

Down
1 Wrong (5)
2 Purchase of a company by another (11)
3 Magnitude of a sound (8)
4 Divisions of companies (11)
5 Stanza of a poem (5)
8 Exuberant merriment (8)
11 Nationality of Stanislas Wawrinka (5)
12 Worship; venerate (5)

No. 109
Tuesday April 19th 2022

Across

1 Disciple (8)
6 Shrub fence (5)
7 Entrance barriers (5)
9 Seabird (4)
10 Eastern temple (6)
12 Public speaker (6)
14 Country bordered by Libya and Sudan (4)
17 Go swiftly (5)
18 Gave a job to (5)
19 Aided (8)

Down

2 More mature (5)
3 Welsh emblem (4)
4 Conical tent (6)
5 Imitative of the past (5)
6 Sausages in bread rolls (3,4)
8 Burnt (7)
11 Paths (6)
13 Smell (5)
15 Vast multitude (5)
16 Resistance units (4)

No. 110
Wednesday April 20th 2022

Across

1 Tools for drilling holes in rocks (6)
4 Type of air pollution (4)
7 Endures (5)
8 Circular in shape (5)
9 Disguises or covers (7)
11 Prove; attest (7)
13 Parts of legs (5)
14 Love affair (5)
15 Musical or vocal sound (4)
16 ___ up: botches or bungles (6)

Down

1 Bands worn around the waist (5)
2 Limitation (11)
3 Recourses (anag) (9)
5 Very large (11)
6 Dizzy (5)
8 Become evident again (9)
10 Go to see (5)
12 Threads or fibres (5)

No. 111
Thursday April 21st 2022

Across

2 Gathered ripened crops (9)
7 Large dark antelope (3)
8 People who fix cars (9)
9 Coming into view (9)
10 Complicated procedure (9)
11 Guitarlike instrument (9)
13 Snare or trap (3)
14 Self-confidence (9)

Down

1 Fear of open spaces (11)
2 Bustle (3)
3 Having four right angles (of a shape) (11)
4 Giant aerial (anag) (11)
5 Unspecified object (5)
6 Making uneasy (11)
10 Turns over and over (5)
12 Mature (3)

No. 112
Friday April 22nd 2022

Across

1 Luminous (10)
6 Taking a long time (4)
7 Strong (6)
8 Go out of a place (6)
9 Elephant tooth (4)
11 Computer virus (4)
13 Treelike grass (6)
15 Violin (6)
17 Find pleasant (4)
18 Evident; apparent (10)

Down

2 Quick musical tempo (7)
3 Sowed (anag) (5)
4 Number after seven (5)
5 Very small child (3)
7 Title of a married woman (3)
10 Breathing aid in water (7)
12 In the middle of (5)
13 Farewell remark (3)
14 Mediterranean island (5)
16 Charged particle (3)

No. 113
Saturday April 23rd 2022

Across

2 Nonconformist (7)
6 Part of a plant (4)
9 Domestic animal (3)
10 Triangle with three unequal sides (7)
11 Not having a written constitution (11)
12 Statement of transactions (7)
13 Nocturnal mammal (3)
14 Correct; accurate (4)
15 Interminable (7)

Down

1 Enjoyable (11)
3 Indignant (9)
4 Machine with keys (10)
5 Fully settled (3,3,5)
7 Related; connected (10)
8 Formal procession (9)

No. 114
Sunday April 24th 2022

Across

6 Make impure (11)
7 Wading birds (5)
9 Confronts; deals with (5)
10 Text accompanying a cartoon (7)
13 Coming after (5)
14 Courageous (5)
15 Leader in a race (5,6)

Down

1 Twenty (5)
2 Merger (11)
3 Trifling (8)
4 Compelling (11)
5 Wild animal; monster (5)
8 Discrete; distinct (8)
11 Light downy particles (5)
12 Aromatic resin (5)

No. 115
Monday April 25th 2022

Across

1 Member of the Christian clergy (9)
6 Pretend (5)
7 Chopped finely (5)
9 Taken as a whole (7)
12 End result (7)
16 Speculate (5)
17 Stuck together (5)
18 Diligent (9)

Down

2 Single entity (4)
3 Major African river (5)
4 ___ Ure: Ultravox singer (5)
5 Sugary flower secretion (6)
6 220 yards (7)
8 Postponed (7)
10 Vitality (3)
11 Greek goddess (6)
13 Fertile spots in deserts (5)
14 ___ on : encouraged (5)
15 Greek spirit (4)

No. 116
Tuesday April 26th 2022

Across

3 Confuse (6)
6 Empty area; gap (5)
7 Public collection of books (7)
9 Regal (5)
12 Chance concurrence of events (11)
14 Strong ringing sound (5)
15 Painting medium (7)
17 Horse's cry (5)
18 Lived with as a guest (6)

Down

1 Large flightless bird (7)
2 Look after an infant (7)
3 Eager and ready to fight (9)
4 Soft animal hair (3)
5 Currency of France and Germany (4)
8 Outdoor platform for musicians (9)
10 Live in (7)
11 Very long (7)
13 Examine by touch (4)
16 Seed vessel (3)

No. 117
Wednesday April 27th 2022

Across

1 Restriction (10)
5 Recorded on video (5)
7 Projecting horizontal ledge (5)
9 Group of seven (6)
10 Slightly open (4)
12 Matures (4)
13 Entreated; beseeched (6)
16 Eighth Greek letter (5)
17 Venomous snake (5)
18 Customs (10)

Down

1 Water lily (5)
2 Cleaned up (6)
3 Check; exam (4)
4 Elated (9)
6 Person who operates marionettes (9)
8 Pro (3)
11 Imagined whilst asleep (6)
12 Small social insect (3)
14 Challenges (5)
15 Attack at speed (4)

No. 118
Thursday April 28th 2022

Across

1 Calm and sensible (5-6)
7 The feel of a surface (7)
8 Spike used by a climber (5)
9 Receive a ball in one's hands (5)
11 Admirable (5)
12 Undertaking something (5)
13 Tough animal tissue (7)
16 Moved to another place (11)

Down

1 Ignited (3)
2 Annoy (3)
3 Nitrous oxide (8,3)
4 Enormous (11)
5 Move; agitate (7)
6 Diminish (7)
9 Direct an orchestra (7)
10 Country in North Africa (7)
14 Rocky hill (3)
15 Extremity (3)

No. 119
Friday April 29th 2022

Across
6 Fabricate (11)
7 Strong thread (5)
9 Small boat (5)
10 Group of figures representing a scene (7)
13 Leashes (5)
14 Mixture that insulates soil (5)
15 Plan beforehand (11)

Down
1 Friendship (5)
2 Gained access to surreptitiously (11)
3 Frozen dessert (3,5)
4 Sudden large increase (7,4)
5 Precious stone (5)
8 Decorated with a raised design (8)
11 Slumbered (5)
12 Impertinence (5)

No. 120
Saturday April 30th 2022

Across
1 Power to do something (10)
5 Car windscreen cleaner (5)
7 Taming of the ___ : Shakespeare play (5)
9 Moved rhythmically to music (6)
10 Religious act (4)
12 Plant fibre (4)
13 Trust or faith in (6)
16 Edge of a knife (5)
17 Inadequately (5)
18 Lose one's job (3,3,4)

Down
1 Intimidated and weakened (5)
2 Heavy load (6)
3 Tilt to one side (4)
4 Very scared (9)
6 Pierce (9)
8 Very small (3)
11 Frail (6)
12 Triangular sail (3)
14 Traditional English breakfast (3-2)
15 Temporary outside shelter (4)

No. 121
Sunday May 1st 2022

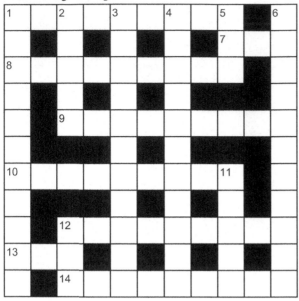

Across

1 Deceptive statement (4-5)
7 Midge ___ : Scottish musician (3)
8 Underwater vessel (9)
9 Doubt about someone's honesty (9)
10 Person engaged in spaceflight (9)
12 Characteristic of an entity (9)
13 Burdensome charge (3)
14 Puts at risk (9)

Down

1 Business of entertaining visitors (11)
2 Parts of the cerebrum (5)
3 Moved goods (11)
4 Designed for usefulness (11)
5 Gradation of colour (3)
6 Helpless (11)
11 Armistice (5)
12 Chopping tool (3)

No. 122
Monday May 2nd 2022

Across

1 Large terrestrial monkey (6)
4 A man (4)
7 Social division in some societies (5)
8 Contrapuntal composition (5)
9 Vacation (7)
11 Irritated (7)
13 ___ du Beke: ballroom dancer (5)
14 Feeling pleased and satisfied (5)
15 Carlos ___ : former tennis player (4)
16 Deduces from evidence (6)

Down

1 Group of goods produced at one time (5)
2 Wonderfully (11)
3 In the red (9)
5 The rules of the road (7,4)
6 Squeeze (5)
8 Wok (6,3)
10 Misgiving (5)
12 Extinct birds (5)

No. 123
Tuesday May 3rd 2022

Across

1 Strip of leather worn round the waist (4)
3 In mint condition (6)
7 One who avoids animal products (5)
9 Explosive devices (5)
10 Groups together (7)
11 Having folds (of a garment) (7)
13 Australian marsupial (5)
14 Retail stores (5)
15 Repudiated (6)
16 Poses a question (4)

Down

1 Tool for marking angles (5)
2 Deception (11)
4 Worms used to control pests (9)
5 Sanctimonious (11)
6 Work tables (5)
8 Discuss the terms of a deal (9)
11 Prodded (5)
12 Stinging insects (5)

No. 124
Wednesday May 4th 2022

Across

1 Makes better (11)
8 More secure (5)
9 Early Christian teacher (7)
10 Ongoing disagreement (11)
13 Rich white cheese (7)
14 Stadium (5)
15 Tries out novel ideas (11)

Down

2 Issue instructions (6)
3 Water storage facility (9)
4 Bunch of threads (4)
5 Examining closely (9)
6 Inoculate (9)
7 Extinct flying reptile (9)
11 Go back (6)
12 Derive the benefits (4)

No. 125
Thursday May 5th 2022

Across

1 Unconventional (of a person) (9)
6 Theme for a discussion (5)
7 The Hunter (constellation) (5)
9 Kitchen implement (7)
12 Elongated rectangles (7)
16 Fast (5)
17 Unexpected plot element (5)
18 Stamina (9)

Down

2 Cloak of a priest (4)
3 Narrow pieces of land (5)
4 Dry red wine (5)
5 Arm strengthening exercise (4-2)
6 Camera stands (7)
8 Closest (7)
10 Breed of dog (3)
11 Flatfish (6)
13 Observed (5)
14 Woodland god (5)
15 Big cat (4)

No. 126
Friday May 6th 2022

Across

1 Correct to the last detail (4-7)
7 Non-specific (7)
8 Double-reed instruments (5)
9 Broom made of twigs (5)
11 Creative thoughts (5)
12 Artificial waterway (5)
13 State of the USA (7)
16 Spanish tennis star (6,5)

Down

1 Hairpiece (3)
2 Hurried (3)
3 Walk round a place (11)
4 Gratitude; acclaim (11)
5 Approve or support (7)
6 Tough questions (7)
9 Meat seller (7)
10 Incidental result of a larger project (4-3)
14 Not new (3)
15 Pointed tool (3)

No. 127
Saturday May 7th 2022

Across
1 Easily made angry (3-8)
8 Wanderer (5)
9 Frees from an obligation (7)
10 Painting genre (8,3)
13 Take a seat (3,4)
14 Dens (5)
15 Going on and on (5-6)

Down
2 Multiples of twelve (6)
3 Oppress; mistreat (9)
4 Talk wildly (4)
5 Managing or governing (9)
6 Athletic contest with ten events (9)
7 Tyrant (9)
11 Long-legged rodent (6)
12 Capital of Ukraine (4)

No. 128
Sunday May 8th 2022

Across
1 Metabolic equilibrium (11)
7 Precisely (7)
8 Relit (anag) (5)
9 Swagger (5)
12 Russian country house (5)
13 Angered; irritated (5)
14 Procedure; standard (7)
16 Skilled drawer (11)

Down
1 Jostled (7)
2 Soft-bodied invertebrate (7)
3 Domineering (11)
4 Diaphanous (11)
5 Took an exam (3)
6 Asian sauce (3)
10 Get back (7)
11 Hierarchical (3-4)
14 Primary colour (3)
15 ___ Thurman: Hollywood star (3)

No. 129
Monday May 9th 2022

Across
1 Deep respect (9)
5 Swiss city (6)
7 Part of the eye (4)
8 Cork for sealing a bottle (7)
11 Eternal (7)
14 Tailless amphibian (4)
15 Exclusive stories (6)
16 Artificial sweetener (9)

Down
1 Finery (7)
2 Year in which wine was produced (7)
3 Hard and brittle (5)
4 Travel by horse (4)
6 Painters (7)
9 Mechanical keyboard (7)
10 Retaliatory action (7)
12 Spiritual teacher (4)
13 Company emblems (5)

No. 130
Tuesday May 10th 2022

Across
6 Spoken communication (4,2,5)
7 The spirit of a people (5)
9 Praise enthusiastically (5)
10 Steal (7)
13 One-way flow structure (5)
14 Iron alloy (5)
15 Lacking seriousness (11)

Down
1 Possessor (5)
2 Group of islands (11)
3 Roman leaders (8)
4 Innovative or pioneering (7,4)
5 During (5)
8 Snakes (8)
11 Lives (anag) (5)
12 Shallow circular dish (5)

No. 131
Wednesday May 11th 2022

Across

6 Caused to stop temporarily (11)
7 ___ Andronicus: Shakespeare play (5)
8 Freight (5)
9 Biggest (7)
12 Pale brownish-yellow colour (5)
13 Traveller on horseback (5)
14 Without guilt (11)

Down

1 Ski run (5)
2 Aristocratic mansion (7,4)
3 Jam or marmalade (8)
4 Having celebrities in attendance (4-7)
5 Goodbye (Spanish) (5)
8 Bright red fruits (8)
10 Fret (5)
11 Smash into another vehicle (5)

No. 132
Thursday May 12th 2022

Across

2 Looked quickly (7)
6 Unit of linear measure (4)
9 Throat of a voracious animal (3)
10 Highest vantage point of a building (7)
11 Make physically stronger (11)
12 Worry (7)
13 Nothing (3)
14 Corner (4)
15 Decline (7)

Down

1 Unwilling (11)
3 Refrained from an action (9)
4 Grumbled (10)
5 Dejected; discouraged (11)
7 Accounts of historical events (10)
8 Row of trees (9)

No. 133
Friday May 13th 2022

Across

1 Existing in abundance (9)
6 Palpitate (5)
7 Type of chemical bond (5)
9 Receptacle for cigarette residue (7)
12 Brings to effective action (7)
16 Amphibians (5)
17 Expect; think that (5)
18 Believed to be the case (9)

Down

2 Goes wrong (4)
3 Leg bone (5)
4 Complete trust (5)
5 Passenger ships (6)
6 Walked upon (7)
8 Hot pepper (7)
10 Wily (3)
11 Lays eggs (6)
13 Drives out from a place (5)
14 Took illegally (5)
15 Unit of liquid capacity (4)

No. 134
Saturday May 14th 2022

Across

2 Steeps in liquid (7)
6 Short sleeps (4)
9 Depression (3)
10 Group of assistants (7)
11 The Archer (constellation) (11)
12 Decorated (7)
13 Surpass (3)
14 Bond movie (2,2)
15 Wishes for (7)

Down

1 Restrained (11)
3 Ornamental water features (9)
4 Rattlesnake (10)
5 Assumption (11)
7 Chunks of written text (10)
8 Merchant who sells writing materials (9)

No. 135
Sunday May 15th 2022

Across
1 Set up or found (9)
5 Using all one's resources (3,3)
7 Small amphibian (4)
8 Discard from memory (7)
11 Modelling runway (7)
14 Metal fastener (4)
15 Long mountain chain (6)
16 Spread widely (of an idea) (9)

Down
1 Flexible (7)
2 Greatest in height (7)
3 Eg taste or touch (5)
4 Pitcher (4)
6 Prickles (7)
9 European country (7)
10 Tell a story (7)
12 Social insects (4)
13 Long-legged bird (5)

No. 136
Monday May 16th 2022

Across *
6 Factual TV program (11)
7 ___ Robson: British tennis player (5)
8 ___ Midler: US singer-songwriter (5)
9 Placing in position (7)
12 South American country (5)
13 Post (5)
14 Very vocal (4-7)

Down
1 Strangely (5)
2 Delicious (11)
3 Fortify against attack (8)
4 Practice of drawing maps (11)
5 Ancient harps (5)
8 Heavenly (8)
10 Climb (5)
11 Unwanted plants (5)

No. 137
Tuesday May 17th 2022

Across
1 Consecutive (4-2-4)
5 Gain new knowledge (5)
7 Manners of walking (5)
9 Over there (6)
10 Doubtful (4)
12 Lisp (anag) (4)
13 Fleet of ships (6)
16 Abrupt (5)
17 Juicy fruit (5)
18 Coating (10)

Down
1 Stomach (5)
2 Type of bicycle (6)
3 Flexible containers (4)
4 Clan leader (9)
6 Ridge of the Himalayas (9)
8 Hit high into the air (3)
11 Formulates a plan (6)
12 Allow (3)
14 In the company of (5)
15 Gradually deprive of milk (4)

No. 138
Wednesday May 18th 2022

Across
1 Decline to do something; rubbish (6)
4 Circular storage medium (4)
7 Anxious (5)
8 State of nervous excitement; high temperature (5)
9 Version of a book (7)
11 Aims or purposes (7)
13 Nick ___ : politician (5)
14 Seat of authority (5)
15 Kiln for drying hops (4)
16 Engaged in games (6)

Down
1 Extent or limit (5)
2 Absolution (11)
3 Jumping from an aeroplane (9)
5 Unintentional (11)
6 Complains continually (5)
8 Enthusiastic to the point of obsession (9)
10 Piece of code to automate a task (5)
12 Very small amount (5)

No. 139
Thursday May 19th 2022

Across

2 Luggage items (9)
7 Touch gently (3)
8 Semiaquatic reptile (9)
9 Type of puzzle (9)
10 Relating to the ear (9)
11 Physical matter (9)
13 Made-up statement (3)
14 Criterion (9)

Down

1 Awfully (11)
2 Health resort (3)
3 Elucidates by using an example (11)
4 Experts on a subject (11)
5 Satisfied a desire (5)
6 Tool; cocktail (11)
10 Natural yellow resin (5)
12 Large deer (3)

No. 140
Friday May 20th 2022

Across

2 Lubricates (7)
5 Woody-stemmed plant (5)
6 Small loudspeaker (7)
7 Coarse (5)
10 Shade of blue (11)
12 Crazy (5)
13 Provoked; encouraged (7)
14 Sprites (5)
15 Sparkle (7)

Down

1 Motivate (7)
2 Entrance (7)
3 So be it (4)
4 Calmly (8)
7 Stirring (8)
8 Wash and iron (7)
9 Imaginary (7)
11 Sword handle (4)

No. 141
Saturday May 21st 2022

Across

1 Lacking humility (8)
6 Large residence (5)
7 Change (5)
9 A strengthened and defended building (4)
10 Sporting venues (6)
12 Distinctive uniform (6)
14 Loot (4)
17 Tall and slim (5)
18 Trudged through water (5)
19 Split apart (8)

Down

2 Underground worker (5)
3 Mythical giant (4)
4 Makes a bill law (6)
5 Pattern (5)
6 Scarf (7)
8 Hauled (7)
11 Stick of coloured wax (6)
13 Naves (anag) (5)
15 Chunk (5)
16 Affectedly dainty (4)

No. 142
Sunday May 22nd 2022

Across

2 Places of worship (7)
5 Overly self-confident (5)
6 Schedule of activities (7)
7 Well-mannered (5)
10 Form into a cluster (11)
12 State of the USA (5)
13 Put in order (7)
14 Avoid (5)
15 Reasons for thinking something (7)

Down

1 Flog; whip (7)
2 Tropical cyclone (7)
3 Short pins that taper at one end (4)
4 Straw hat (8)
7 Colliding with (8)
8 In addition to (7)
9 Yellow fruits (7)
11 Boyfriend (4)

No. 143
Monday May 23rd 2022

Across

6 Underwear (5,6)
7 Not illuminated (5)
8 Brass instrument (5)
9 Pipe (7)
12 Solemn promises (5)
13 Body of rules (5)
14 Temporary (11)

Down

1 Paula ____ : US singer (5)
2 Elucidation of an idea (11)
3 Feigns (8)
4 Scaring (11)
5 County in SE England (5)
8 Reliable stock market company (4,4)
10 Shallow ice-cream dish (5)
11 Genuflected (5)

No. 144
Tuesday May 24th 2022

Across

1 Sews (8)
6 Skewered meat (5)
7 Stiff (5)
9 Type of golf club (4)
10 Agreement or concord (6)
12 Makes spick and span (6)
14 Hindu spiritual discipline (4)
17 Fits of violent anger (5)
18 High-pitched noises (5)
19 Lessening; diminishing (8)

Down

2 Prohibited by social custom (5)
3 Brass instrument (4)
4 Employing (6)
5 Road information boards (5)
6 Needleworker (7)
8 Disavowals; rebuttals (7)
11 Ship (6)
13 Principle laid down by an authority (5)
15 Eg Pacific or Atlantic (5)
16 Comply with an order (4)

No. 145
Wednesday May 25th 2022

Across

1 Person who fells trees (10)
5 Town in Surrey (5)
7 ___ Klum: supermodel (5)
9 Fish with pink flesh (6)
10 Set of playing cards (4)
12 Jedi Master in Star Wars films (4)
13 Arranged like rays (6)
16 ___-soprano: singing voice (5)
17 Variety of viola (5)
18 Incidentally (10)

Down

1 City in West Yorkshire (5)
2 Implant deeply (6)
3 Fourth Gospel (4)
4 Standard by which a thing is judged (9)
6 Six (4-5)
8 Fountain pen contents (3)
11 Maples (anag) (6)
12 Sweet potato (3)
14 Roadside area (3-2)
15 ___ Berra: baseball player (4)

No. 146
Thursday May 26th 2022

Across

1 Sacred (anag) (6)
4 Moist (4)
7 Empty spaces (5)
8 Thing that imparts motion (5)
9 Caring for (7)
11 Comic film with Jim Carrey and Cameron Diaz (3,4)
13 Eg cumulus (5)
14 Suffuse with colour (5)
15 Opposite of more (4)
16 Without ethics (6)

Down

1 Assembly of witches (5)
2 These are put up at Christmas (11)
3 Very thin and bony (9)
5 Small room that leads to a main one (11)
6 Dodge (a question) (5)
8 Metallic element (9)
10 Pertaining to the voice (5)
12 Ring solemnly (5)

No. 147
Friday May 27th 2022

Across
- **1** The squandering of money (11)
- **7** Speak rhetorically (7)
- **8** Explode (5)
- **9** Bed cover (5)
- **11** Removes the lid (5)
- **12** Tailored fold (5)
- **13** Fragrant compound (7)
- **16** Unnecessary; superfluous (11)

Down
- **1** Performed an action (3)
- **2** Dry (of wine) (3)
- **3** Heedless (11)
- **4** The military (5,6)
- **5** Satisfy a desire (7)
- **6** Tidies (7)
- **9** Smacked (7)
- **10** Uses up energy (7)
- **14** Arrest; apprehend (3)
- **15** First woman (3)

No. 148
Saturday May 28th 2022

Across
- **2** Insipid and bland (9)
- **7** Consumed food (3)
- **8** Onset of darkness (9)
- **9** Principal church of a diocese (9)
- **10** Purgation of emotions (9)
- **11** Employees (9)
- **13** Era (anag) (3)
- **14** Cherished (9)

Down
- **1** Legendary transport device (5,6)
- **2** Nine plus one (3)
- **3** Proposals (11)
- **4** Performer (11)
- **5** Electronic message (5)
- **6** Confident (4-7)
- **10** Swerve; bend (5)
- **12** Boy (3)

No. 149
Sunday May 29th 2022

Across

1 Combustible (11)
8 Evil spirit (5)
9 Free from doubt (7)
10 Coordinate (11)
13 Grassland (7)
14 Ballroom dance (5)
15 Made to order (6-5)

Down

2 Material; textile (6)
3 Natural charm or appealing quality (9)
4 Ill-mannered person (4)
5 Brightened up (9)
6 Very athletic (9)
7 Sport played in a pool (5,4)
11 Former pupils (6)
12 Antelopes (4)

No. 150
Monday May 30th 2022

Across

1 Nostalgic (11)
7 Baltic country (7)
8 Fixed platform by water (5)
9 Small nails (5)
12 Old French currency (5)
13 Covers with gold (5)
14 Mix (7)
16 Discernible (11)

Down

1 Exhibitionist (4-3)
2 ___ Bedingfield: musician (7)
3 Not achieving results (11)
4 Property professional (6,5)
5 Light brown colour (3)
6 Mauna ___ : Hawaiian volcano (3)
10 SI unit of electric charge (7)
11 Let up (7)
14 Edible mushroom (3)
15 Make imperfect (3)

No. 151
Tuesday May 31st 2022

Across
1 Legendary tales (6)
4 Graphic symbol (4)
7 In a ___ : very quickly (5)
8 Relating to the kidneys (5)
9 Fails to act decisively (7)
11 Moving forward at speed (7)
13 States to be the case (5)
14 ___ Allan Poe: American writer (5)
15 Current of air (4)
16 Steady (anag) (6)

Down
1 Stinky (5)
2 Fragility (11)
3 Morning break (informal) (9)
5 Bewilderingly (11)
6 Synthetic fibre (5)
8 Revitalise (9)
10 Loud metallic sound (5)
12 Pierced by a bull's horn (5)

No. 152
Wednesday June 1st 2022

Across
1 Top boat in a fleet (8)
6 Urticaria (5)
7 Care for; look after (5)
9 Left side of a ship (4)
10 Majestic (6)
12 One or the other of two (6)
14 Primates (4)
17 Sisal (anag) (5)
18 Practice of lending money at high interest rates (5)
19 Diabolically cruel (8)

Down
2 Organ (5)
3 Flow copiously (4)
4 Terminate a telephone call (4,2)
5 Clean spiritually (5)
6 Unfortunate (7)
8 Diplomatic building (7)
11 Person to whom a lease is granted (6)
13 Robber (5)
15 Purple fruits (5)
16 Regretted (4)

No. 153
Thursday June 2nd 2022

Across

6 Shipment (11)
7 Wound the pride of (5)
9 Bring to the conscious mind (5)
10 Entered in a hostile manner (7)
13 Go about stealthily (5)
14 Narcotics (5)
15 Re-evaluation (11)

Down

1 Long flower-stalk (5)
2 Unambiguous (11)
3 Not necessary (8)
4 Try to predict an outcome (6-5)
5 Spread by scattering (5)
8 Wrapper for a letter (8)
11 Dramatic musical work (5)
12 Lyrical poem or song (5)

No. 154
Friday June 3rd 2022

Across

1 Series of links on a web page (10)
6 Wire lattice (4)
7 First appearances (6)
8 Small pet canine (6)
9 Eg pecan and cashew (4)
11 Finish (4)
13 Wet (6)
15 Fly an aircraft (6)
17 Imitated (4)
18 Wipe out (10)

Down

2 Bring a law into effect again (2-5)
3 Hankered after (5)
4 Living in a city (5)
5 Mouthpiece attached to a bridle (3)
7 Excavate (3)
10 Severe mental suffering (7)
12 Crustacean like a shrimp (5)
13 Great distress (3)
14 Fishing net (5)
16 By way of (3)

No. 155
Saturday June 4th 2022

Across

3 Legitimate (6)
6 Monster with nine heads (5)
7 On wings (anag) (7)
9 Opposite of tall (5)
12 Instrument for recording heart activity (11)
14 Certain to fail (2-3)
15 Windpipe (7)
17 Follow the position of (5)
18 Quash; tame (6)

Down

1 Science of matter and energy (7)
2 Postpone (7)
3 Denoting a final attempt (4-5)
4 Not many (3)
5 Breathing organ (4)
8 Arise; start (9)
10 Small Arctic whale (7)
11 Water passage (7)
13 Vases (4)
16 Edible nut (3)

No. 156
Sunday June 5th 2022

Across

1 Deliberate (11)
7 Young cats (7)
8 Shabby and worn (5)
9 Pertaining to the ear (5)
11 Cooks (5)
12 Italian cathedral (5)
13 Existing at the beginning (7)
16 Prevent from continuing (4,3,4)

Down

1 Family or variety (3)
2 Exclamation of contempt (3)
3 Embroidery (11)
4 Done without thinking (11)
5 Bring up; rear (7)
6 Legal practitioners (7)
9 Deliver by parachute (3-4)
10 Act of getting rid of something (7)
14 Not well (3)
15 Carry a heavy object (3)

No. 157
Monday June 6th 2022

Across

1 Attract powerfully (6)
4 Examine quickly (4)
7 View (5)
8 Jessica ___-Hill : British heptathlete (5)
9 Extend an arm or leg (7)
11 Competitors in a sprint (7)
13 Daisy-like flower (5)
14 Visual representation (5)
15 Calf-length skirt (4)
16 Wading birds (6)

Down

1 Rescues (5)
2 Shared out (11)
3 Loquacious talker (9)
5 Thoughtful (11)
6 Facial protuberances (5)
8 Improving (9)
10 Assert that something is the case (5)
12 Prophets (5)

No. 158
Tuesday June 7th 2022

Across

6 Integrity; trustworthiness (11)
7 Follows orders (5)
9 Additional (5)
10 Insert in a person's body (7)
13 Arboreal primate (5)
14 Cleanse by rubbing (5)
15 Impurity (11)

Down

1 Stage performer (5)
2 Act of harassing someone (11)
3 Inorganic nutrients (8)
4 Autocratic (11)
5 Local authority rule (2-3)
8 Cartoon character who can fly (8)
11 Pull out a hair (5)
12 Assists in a crime (5)

No. 159
Wednesday June 8th 2022

Across
1 A wine shop (6)
4 Eg an arm or leg (4)
7 Craftsman who uses stone (5)
8 ___ days: the distant past (5)
9 Electronic retention of data (7)
11 Edible marine molluscs (7)
13 Bring together (5)
14 Large waterbirds (5)
15 Obscures (4)
16 Stationary part of a motor (6)

Down
1 Knocks into (5)
2 Finding (11)
3 Study of ancestry (9)
5 Unconcerned (11)
6 Young rabbit (5)
8 Careless omission (9)
10 Cram (5)
12 Give a solemn oath (5)

No. 160
Thursday June 9th 2022

Across
2 Form or accumulate steadily (5-2)
5 Longest river in Europe (5)
6 Back pain (7)
7 Essential (5)
10 A parent's Dad (11)
12 Local sporting match (5)
13 Prophets (7)
14 Large African antelope (5)
15 Bright red (7)

Down
1 Floating wreckage (7)
2 Slow romantic songs (7)
3 Aerial tennis shots (4)
4 Belongings (8)
7 Strong; full of energy (8)
8 Mobile phone (7)
9 Relating to heat (7)
11 Mark left from a wound (4)

No. 161
Friday June 10th 2022

Across

1 Extremely impressive (11)
7 Chaser (7)
8 Sound of any kind (5)
9 In front (5)
11 Basins (5)
12 Common greeting (5)
13 Equilateral parallelogram (7)
16 Alliance (11)

Down

1 Conciliatory gift (3)
2 Organ of hearing (3)
3 Masterpiece (4,2,5)
4 Fundamental feature (11)
5 Secret affair (7)
6 Returns to a former state (7)
9 Old-fashioned (7)
10 Give reasons for (7)
14 Bleat of a sheep (3)
15 Utter (3)

No. 162
Saturday June 11th 2022

Across

2 Small mat (7)
5 Bony structure in the head (5)
6 Drug that relieves pain (7)
7 Gives as a reference (5)
10 Act of working together (11)
12 Concur (5)
13 Restless (7)
14 Arm joint (5)
15 Perfumed (7)

Down

1 Disturbance; commotion (7)
2 Categories (7)
3 Read quickly (4)
4 Repudiate (8)
7 Large hard-shelled oval nuts (8)
8 Left a building (7)
9 Microorganism (7)
11 Char (4)

No. 163
Sunday June 12th 2022

Across
1 Incapable of being split (11)
8 Chopping (5)
9 A number defining position (7)
10 Tumultuous (11)
13 Fall back (7)
14 Expressed clearly (5)
15 Beyond acceptability (3,2,6)

Down
2 Crown (6)
3 Idle chatter (5,4)
4 Projecting edge (4)
5 Totally absorbed by (9)
6 Case (9)
7 Unprecedented (7-2)
11 Dispute the truth of (6)
12 Short tail (4)

No. 164
Monday June 13th 2022

Across
6 Component part (11)
7 Rushes (5)
9 Strong lightweight wood (5)
10 Simple sugar (7)
13 Girls ___ : pop group (5)
14 Character in the musical Oliver! (5)
15 Agreement (11)

Down
1 Frightening (5)
2 Below the planet's surface (11)
3 Resolute (8)
4 Having good intentions (4-7)
5 Thick slice of meat (5)
8 Operational unit in an air force (8)
11 Seasoning (5)
12 Used a computer keyboard (5)

No. 165
Tuesday June 14th 2022

Across

1 Pursuit of high principles (8)
6 Makes beer (5)
7 Sweet-scented shrub (5)
9 On top of (4)
10 Whipped cream dessert (6)
12 Extremely fashionable; scalding (3-3)
14 ___ Khan: British boxer (4)
17 Jumps into water (5)
18 Kirstie ___ : US actress (5)
19 Toneless (anag) (8)

Down

2 ___ Maradona: footballer (5)
3 Too; in addition (4)
4 Ice homes (6)
5 Thaws (5)
6 Fuzzy (7)
8 Obviously (7)
11 Form-fitting garment (6)
13 Backless sofa (5)
15 Shopping centres (US) (5)
16 Spherical object (4)

No. 166
Wednesday June 15th 2022

Across

6 Imaginable (11)
7 Studies a subject at university (5)
9 Crawl (5)
10 Traditional piano keys (7)
13 Respond to (5)
14 Mallet (5)
15 Dishonestly (11)

Down

1 Skin marks from wounds (5)
2 Occupancy (11)
3 Ejecting (8)
4 Compulsively (11)
5 Tidily kept (5)
8 Thick drink (8)
11 Group of lions (5)
12 Takes part in a game (5)

No. 167
Thursday June 16th 2022

Across
1 Angelic (8)
6 Titled (5)
7 Type of jazz (5)
9 Resident of an abbey (4)
10 Pertaining to the mind (6)
12 Blunt needle (6)
14 Fill to capacity (4)
17 Reason for innocence (5)
18 Style of Greek architecture (5)
19 Vehicle with three wheels (8)

Down
2 Mortal (5)
3 Fishing sticks (4)
4 Very young children (6)
5 Ancient measure of length (5)
6 African country (7)
8 Strong verbal attack (7)
11 Minimal bathing suit (6)
13 Believer in a supreme being (5)
15 Rustic (5)
16 Movement of water causing a small whirlpool (4)

No. 168
Friday June 17th 2022

Across
1 Engrave with acid (4)
3 Ploys (6)
7 Drab (5)
9 Aqualung (5)
10 Shutting (7)
11 Lifted (7)
13 Snake toxin (5)
14 Fluffy and soft (5)
15 Gaseous envelope of the sun (6)
16 Salver (4)

Down
1 Senior figure in a tribe (5)
2 Substance applied to hair (11)
4 Replied (9)
5 Vegetable (11)
6 Very informal phrases (5)
8 Sailor of a light vessel (9)
11 Total disorder (5)
12 Craftily (5)

No. 169
Saturday June 18th 2022

Across

1 Beginning (8)
6 Respected person in a field (5)
7 Island in the Mediterranean Sea (5)
9 Locate or place (4)
10 Rarely (6)
12 Follows (6)
14 Legume (4)
17 Adjusted the pitch of (5)
18 Loft (5)
19 Free from dirt; hygienic (8)

Down

2 Secret rendezvous (5)
3 Tolled (4)
4 Iridaceous plants (6)
5 Crunch; wear down (5)
6 Express disagreement (7)
8 Yearbook (7)
11 Deprive of force (6)
13 Transmits (5)
15 Go in (5)
16 Without shine; dull (4)

No. 170
Sunday June 19th 2022

Across

6 Suggestion (11)
7 Debate in a heated manner (5)
8 Opposite of lows (5)
9 Look something over closely (7)
12 Seed cases (5)
13 ___ Lavigne: Canadian singer (5)
14 Drug causing a loss of sensation (11)

Down

1 Talk (5)
2 US politician (11)
3 Certain to fail (8)
4 Peculiarity (11)
5 Grind the teeth together (5)
8 Worrying problem (8)
10 Bottle (5)
11 Sudden jerk (5)

No. 171
Monday June 20th 2022

Across
6 Necessary condition (11)
7 Steer (5)
9 Bring into a line (5)
10 Breathed in (7)
13 Electrician (5)
14 Kind of wheat (5)
15 Serving to enlighten; instructive (11)

Down
1 Pond-dwelling amphibians (5)
2 State of balance (11)
3 Elaborate (8)
4 Causing bafflement (11)
5 Large pebble (5)
8 Extremely delicate (8)
11 Possessed (5)
12 Show pleasure facially (5)

No. 172
Tuesday June 21st 2022

Across
1 Culmination (10)
6 Young sheep (4)
7 Stadiums (6)
8 Duplicity (6)
9 Unit of type size (4)
11 Stopper (4)
13 Agricultural implement (6)
15 Turmoil (6)
17 Skit (anag) (4)
18 Give or apply (a remedy) (10)

Down
2 Flat highland (7)
3 Piece of furniture (5)
4 Clean with a brush (5)
5 Large body of water (3)
7 Suitable (3)
10 Chuckle (7)
12 Darkness (5)
13 Female pronoun (3)
14 Garden tools (5)
16 Legume (3)

No. 173
Wednesday June 22nd 2022

Across

1 Cause resentment (8)
6 Follow on (5)
7 Hot rock (5)
9 Eat like a bird (4)
10 Religious act of petition (6)
12 Has confidence in (6)
14 Stiff paper (4)
17 Abominable snowmen (5)
18 Join together; merge (5)
19 Stealing (cattle) (8)

Down

2 Agreeable sound or tune (5)
3 Individual article or unit (4)
4 Stopwatches (6)
5 Popular sport (5)
6 Ability to understand the feelings of another (7)
8 Shorten (7)
11 Stagnation or inactivity (6)
13 Express; complete (5)
15 Pertaining to bees (5)
16 Narrate (4)

No. 174
Thursday June 23rd 2022

Across

2 Tentacled cephalopod (7)
6 Haul (4)
9 Draw (3)
10 Victory (7)
11 Of considerable size (11)
12 Left out (7)
13 Eg almond or pecan (3)
14 A group of three people (4)
15 Released from a duty (7)

Down

1 Youth (11)
3 Finish (9)
4 Pioneer (10)
5 Conjecture (11)
7 Drug that destroys microorganisms (10)
8 Regions (9)

No. 175
Friday June 24th 2022

Across
2 Fishing (7)
5 Cabs (5)
6 Not as big (7)
7 Type of military operation (5)
10 Restlessly (11)
12 Shoot with great precision (5)
13 Sudden inclination to act (7)
14 Exposes to danger (5)
15 Chivalrous (7)

Down
1 Extract (7)
2 Takes a firm stand (7)
3 Gentle accent (4)
4 Grotesquely carved figure (8)
7 Breathing in sharply (8)
8 Sweet course (7)
9 Rattish (anag) (7)
11 Haul (4)

No. 176
Saturday June 25th 2022

Across
2 Instructions on how to cook dishes (7)
6 Slight cut (4)
9 What a spider weaves (3)
10 Insect body segment (7)
11 Poorly behaved; impolite (3-8)
12 System of interconnected things (7)
13 Large (3)
14 Run at a moderate pace (of horses) (4)
15 People who make money (7)

Down
1 Unwise (11)
3 Eucharist (9)
4 Type of moneylender (10)
5 Lower in rank (11)
7 Rival contestant (10)
8 Benefit (9)

No. 177
Sunday June 26th 2022

Across

1 Doubt (10)
6 Raps (anag) (4)
7 Repeat (6)
8 Shun (6)
9 Circuits of a racetrack (4)
11 Golf pegs (4)
13 Walks slowly (6)
15 In flower (6)
17 Comedy sketch (4)
18 Designate (10)

Down

2 Deadlock (7)
3 Mooring for a ship (5)
4 Kick out (5)
5 Long period of time (3)
7 Argument (3)
10 Foretell (7)
12 Exhibited (5)
13 Limb (3)
14 Buffalo (5)
16 Of a low standard (3)

No. 178
Monday June 27th 2022

Across

1 Physically strong and active (8)
6 Loose fibre used in caulking wooden ships (5)
7 Path to follow (5)
9 Walked or stepped (4)
10 Puzzle composed of many pieces (6)
12 Relating to the lower back (6)
14 Having inherent ability (4)
17 Timepiece (5)
18 Turns (anag) (5)
19 Hopefulness about the future (8)

Down

2 Capital of Japan (5)
3 Feeble (of an excuse) (4)
4 Tasty morsel (6)
5 Converses casually (5)
6 Effluence (7)
8 Anarchic (7)
11 Official seal (6)
13 Underground railway (5)
15 Makes fast with ropes (5)
16 Neat in appearance (4)

No. 179
Tuesday June 28th 2022

Across

1 Act of going before in time (11)
8 Frustrated and annoyed (3,2)
9 Person who shows no gratitude (7)
10 200th anniversary of an event (11)
13 Nocturnal carnivorous mammal (7)
14 Snow home (5)
15 Advance quickly (4-7)

Down

2 Calamitous (6)
3 Civility; respect (9)
4 Dons (anag) (4)
5 Giving a job to (9)
6 Incredulity (9)
7 Impervious to water (9)
11 Single-celled organism (6)
12 Mountain system in Europe (4)

No. 180
Wednesday June 29th 2022

Across

1 Type of tea (10)
5 Thin crisp biscuit (5)
7 Ostentatious glamour (5)
9 Gentle sheen (6)
10 Spun thread used for knitting (4)
12 Cry of derision (4)
13 Surgical knife (6)
16 Delicious (5)
17 Helmet part for protecting the face (5)
18 Fan (10)

Down

1 Lowed (anag) (5)
2 Mistakes (6)
3 Light toboggan (4)
4 Annoying things (9)
6 Anglers (9)
8 School of Mahayana Buddhism (3)
11 Divides in two (6)
12 Happiness (3)
14 Fortune-telling card (5)
15 Legendary story (4)

No. 181
Thursday June 30th 2022

Across

6 Asking (11)
7 Maladroit (5)
8 Started (5)
9 Type of snake (informal) (7)
12 Dislikes intensely (5)
13 ___ Jones: American singer-songwriter (5)
14 Resound (11)

Down

1 Supply with; furnish (5)
2 Piercing; showing insight (11)
3 Written laws (8)
4 ___ man: type of biscuit (11)
5 Extreme pain (5)
8 Well-rounded (8)
10 Have in common (5)
11 There (anag) (5)

No. 182
Friday July 1st 2022

Across

1 Blowfly (10)
5 Blowing in puffs (of wind) (5)
7 Collection of songs (5)
9 At sixes and ___ : in disarray (6)
10 Make beer or ale (4)
12 Search for (4)
13 Pronouncement (6)
16 Pinch; squeeze (5)
17 TV presenters (5)
18 Stand-in performer (10)

Down

1 Counterfeit (5)
2 Purchasing (6)
3 Seat (anag) (4)
4 Frees (9)
6 Legal UK driving age (9)
8 Cut grass (3)
11 Seeks information indirectly (6)
12 Smack (3)
14 ___ Elliott: US singer (5)
15 Island of the Inner Hebrides (4)

No. 183
Saturday July 2nd 2022

Across

1 Wind instrument (10)
6 Unfasten (4)
7 Arrange laws systematically (6)
8 Brusque and irritable (6)
9 Fencing sword (4)
11 Sums together (4)
13 Self-important; arrogant (6)
15 Large lizard (6)
17 Long periods of history (4)
18 Fervent (10)

Down

2 Paid no attention to (7)
3 Very unpleasant (5)
4 Evade (5)
5 Not on (3)
7 Bashful; reluctant to give details (3)
10 Competitor (7)
12 Unexpected catches (5)
13 North American nation (abbrev.) (3)
14 Birds do this to clean their feathers (5)
16 Space or interval (3)

No. 184
Sunday July 3rd 2022

Across

6 Tame (11)
7 ___ DeGeneres: US comedienne (5)
8 Foot joint (5)
9 Film starring Guy Pearce (7)
12 Alcoholic drinks made from grapes (5)
13 Objection; complain (5)
14 Centralised (anag) (11)

Down

1 Gardening tool (5)
2 Petty (5-6)
3 Giant ocean waves (8)
4 Eg Christmas Day (4,7)
5 Surround and harass (5)
8 Renounce or reject (8)
10 Two times (5)
11 ___ Witherspoon: actress (5)

No. 185
Monday July 4th 2022

Across

1 Inattentive (11)
8 Applaud (5)
9 Hanging drapery (7)
10 Cautious (11)
13 Act of awakening from sleep (7)
14 Tease or pester (5)
15 Delightfully (11)

Down

2 Of the eye (6)
3 Period of economic decline (9)
4 Affirm with confidence (4)
5 Entry gate (9)
6 Emptied (9)
7 Operated by air under pressure (9)
11 Frames used by artists (6)
12 Boring (4)

No. 186
Tuesday July 5th 2022

Across

2 Hard-shelled insect pupa (9)
7 Grassland (3)
8 Dutch painter (9)
9 Contemplative people (9)
10 Cell contents excluding the nucleus (9)
11 Intolerance of the opinions of others (9)
13 Statute (3)
14 Cut up (9)

Down

1 Alert and thinking cogently (5-6)
2 Vehicle (3)
3 Censure severely (11)
4 A thing one excels at (6,5)
5 Joins together (5)
6 Official agreements (11)
10 Animal enclosures (5)
12 Deranged (3)

No. 187
Wednesday July 6th 2022

Across

1 Memorial structures (9)
6 Unabridged (5)
7 Grasp tightly (5)
9 Alfresco (4-3)
12 Not tidy (7)
16 Young sheep (5)
17 Promotional wording (5)
18 Alert and aware (9)

Down

2 Narrow strip of land (4)
3 Saying (5)
4 Shallow recess (5)
5 Sailor (6)
6 Not level (7)
8 Agitate (7)
10 Drivel; nonsense (3)
11 With hands on the hips (6)
13 Vertical spars for sails (5)
14 Underground enlarged stem (5)
15 Insect stage (4)

No. 188
Thursday July 7th 2022

Across

1 Atheist (11)
8 Tries out (5)
9 Arrogance; loftiness (7)
10 Having a firm basis in reality (11)
13 Termite (anag) (7)
14 Supply with new weapons (5)
15 Minor crime (11)

Down

2 Residential district (6)
3 Belonging naturally (9)
4 Container for flowers (4)
5 Fruit (9)
6 Spoke very quietly (9)
7 Refined males (9)
11 Confine as a prisoner (6)
12 Pull (4)

No. 189
Friday July 8th 2022

Across
1. Made good on a debt (6)
4. Part of a sleeve (4)
7. Staple food (5)
8. God of love (5)
9. Eg Rebecca Adlington (7)
11. Caused to catch fire (7)
13. High renown (5)
14. Strong thick rope (5)
15. Throw a coin in the air (4)
16. Precious stones (6)

Down
1. Loose outer garments (5)
2. Extremely steep (11)
3. Security against a loss (9)
5. Unappetising (11)
6. Grew fainter (5)
8. Record of events (9)
10. Take part in combat (5)
12. Workers (5)

No. 190
Saturday July 9th 2022

Across
6. Contest (11)
7. Vegetables (5)
9. Eg the Thames (5)
10. Visual display unit (7)
13. Baby carriages (5)
14. Pilfer (5)
15. Orca (6,5)

Down
1. Burn with hot liquid (5)
2. Watertight (11)
3. Ragtimes (anag) (8)
4. Award for coming second (6,5)
5. The Hunting of the ___ : nonsense poem by Lewis Carroll (5)
8. Ominous (8)
11. Talked audibly (5)
12. Worked steadily at (5)

No. 191
Sunday July 10th 2022

Across
1 Praiseworthy (11)
8 Spy (5)
9 Snobbish (7)
10 Reliable (11)
13 Nightdress (7)
14 Rocky; harsh (5)
15 Aimless (11)

Down
2 One's environment (6)
3 Small warship (9)
4 Written work (4)
5 Staff (9)
6 Unsafe structure (9)
7 Nut (9)
11 Steal (6)
12 Whirring sound (4)

No. 192
Monday July 11th 2022

Across
1 Differentiation (11)
7 Very young infant (7)
8 Mother-of-pearl (5)
9 Great sorrow (5)
11 Unfortunately (5)
12 Indoor game (5)
13 Floating mass of frozen water (7)
16 Fear in front of an audience (5,6)

Down
1 University teacher (3)
2 Fasten with stitches (3)
3 Not hurtful (11)
4 Expert critic (11)
5 Freezing (3-4)
6 Flower arrangement (7)
9 Flying vehicles without engines (7)
10 Resistance to change (7)
14 Food item from a hen (3)
15 Acquire; obtain (3)

No. 193
Tuesday July 12th 2022

Across

6 Process of getting ready for use (11)
7 Wanderer (5)
8 Cereal plant (5)
9 Not artificial (7)
12 Outdoor fundraising events (5)
13 Speed (5)
14 Humiliating (11)

Down

1 Rotates (5)
2 Ending (11)
3 Official orders (8)
4 Disenchant (11)
5 Alphabetical list in a book (5)
8 Retailer (8)
10 Attach (5)
11 Dr ___ : US writer (5)

No. 194
Wednesday July 13th 2022

Across

1 Quashed (10)
6 Singe (4)
7 Keyboard instruments (6)
8 Type of nut (6)
9 Rent (4)
11 Limbs used for walking (4)
13 Excursions made for pleasure (6)
15 Worshipper (6)
17 Large town (4)
18 A decrease in loudness (10)

Down

2 Lift up (7)
3 Roofed entrance to a house (5)
4 Tennis stroke (5)
5 Pair of performers (3)
7 Long bench (3)
10 Moved round an axis (7)
12 Go away from quickly (5)
13 Jolt (3)
14 Male relation (5)
16 Father (3)

No. 195
Thursday July 14th 2022

Across

1 Great disgust (10)
5 Country in southern Asia (5)
7 Period of time consisting of 28 - 31 days (5)
9 Nearer in the future (6)
10 Award (informal) (4)
12 Foot of a horse (4)
13 False (6)
16 Tropical fruit (5)
17 Recurrent topic (5)
18 File linked to an email (10)

Down

1 Attacks without warning (5)
2 Covered with a shiny coating (6)
3 Weapons (4)
4 Large gathering of people (9)
6 Substance that reduces perspiration (9)
8 Witch (3)
11 Informer (6)
12 Domesticated pig (3)
14 Pick out; choose (5)
15 Heroic tale (4)

No. 196
Friday July 15th 2022

Across

1 Capital of Argentina (6,5)
7 Persistent problem (7)
8 Egg-shaped solid (5)
9 Animal life of a region (5)
11 This follows day (5)
12 The protection of a particular person (5)
13 Swinging bed (7)
16 Obscurely (11)

Down

1 Hairstyle (3)
2 Unit of energy (3)
3 Straightforward (4-3-4)
4 Streamlined (11)
5 Performing a task again (7)
6 Type of quarry (7)
9 Extreme enthusiast (7)
10 Country in South America (7)
14 Eg Hedwig in Harry Potter (3)
15 Item that unlocks a door (3)

No. 197
Saturday July 16th 2022

Across
1. Made level (8)
6. Men (5)
7. Cake decoration (5)
9. Engage in spirited fun (4)
10. More likely than not (4-2)
12. Opposite of a victory (6)
14. Slightly curling lock of hair (4)
17. Humped ruminant (5)
18. Use to one's advantage (5)
19. Cats coat (anag) (8)

Down
2. Type of tooth (5)
3. Expel; drive out (4)
4. Coiffure (6)
5. Removes moisture (5)
6. Tuneful (7)
8. Respectable; refined (7)
11. Spanish rice dish (6)
13. Exhaust gases (5)
15. Change (5)
16. Mineral powder (4)

No. 198
Sunday July 17th 2022

Across
1. Up-to-date and fashionable (6)
4. Greenish blue colour (4)
7. Eating places (5)
8. Labour organisation (5)
9. Touches the skin of another lightly (7)
11. Screaming (7)
13. Extreme fear (5)
14. ___ Milan: football club (5)
15. Spool-like toy (2-2)
16. Protects from heat (6)

Down
1. Implied without being stated (5)
2. For all practical purposes (11)
3. Showed on a computer (of information) (9)
5. Mentally sharp; astute (5-6)
6. Harass; frustrate (5)
8. Altruistic (9)
10. Risky (5)
12. Microorganisms (5)

No. 199
Monday July 18th 2022

Across
1 Giddiness (9)
5 Easy to understand (6)
7 Bovine animals (4)
8 Pin in a spinning wheel (7)
11 Palest (7)
14 Skating venue (4)
15 Creative act (6)
16 Sweet coverings (9)

Down
1 Deny any responsibility for (7)
2 River of East Africa (7)
3 Faint (5)
4 Head covering (4)
6 Laid open to view (7)
9 Enunciation of speech (7)
10 Short trips to perform tasks (7)
12 Bristle (4)
13 Buyer (5)

No. 200
Tuesday July 19th 2022

Across
6 Cheat someone financially (5-6)
7 Ordered arrangement (5)
9 Run away with a lover (5)
10 Turns red with embarrassment (7)
13 Cruel or severe (5)
14 Imbibe (5)
15 Eg a lemon or lime (6,5)

Down
1 Test or examine a metal (5)
2 Confirm (11)
3 Beat out grain (8)
4 Unintentional (11)
5 More recent (5)
8 Young (8)
11 Throw (5)
12 Move on ice (5)

No. 201
Wednesday July 20th 2022

Across
2 Horizontal angle of a compass bearing (7)
5 Give a false notion of (5)
6 European country (7)
7 Extremely small (prefix) (5)
10 Lack of being (11)
12 Gold block (5)
13 Continue (5,2)
14 Penitent (5)
15 Abandon one's principles (4,3)

Down
1 Appease (7)
2 Type of respiration (7)
3 Ditch filled with water (4)
4 Stocky (8)
7 Curved surface of a liquid in a tube (8)
8 Contrary to (7)
9 Mendicants (7)
11 Spoken exam (4)

No. 202
Thursday July 21st 2022

Across
1 Shortened (11)
7 Public transport vehicle (7)
8 Singing voice (5)
9 Intense light beam (5)
11 Papal court (5)
12 Small decorative balls (5)
13 Become rigid (7)
16 Withdrawal of support (11)

Down
1 Commotion (3)
2 Round bread roll (3)
3 Abashed (11)
4 Direction (11)
5 Loud sound following lightning (7)
6 Small-scale model (7)
9 Brazilian dance (7)
10 Large island of Indonesia (7)
14 Enemy (3)
15 Louse egg (3)

No. 203
Friday July 22nd 2022

Across
- **6** Seaside scavenger (11)
- **7** Individual things (5)
- **9** Lines (anag) (5)
- **10** Large Israeli city (3,4)
- **13** Opposite of best (5)
- **14** A moving part of a generator (5)
- **15** Pun (4,2,5)

Down
- **1** Concerning (5)
- **2** Dictatorial (11)
- **3** Extension of a debt (8)
- **4** Room used by astronomers (11)
- **5** Rub out (5)
- **8** Answer to a problem (8)
- **11** Hit; steal (5)
- **12** Quick and active (5)

No. 204
Saturday July 23rd 2022

Across
- **1** Hallway (8)
- **6** Lacking enthusiasm; weary (5)
- **7** ___ Presley: US singer (5)
- **9** Standard (4)
- **10** ___ Staunton: English actress (6)
- **12** Messengers of God (6)
- **14** Freshwater game fish (4)
- **17** Produce as a fruit (5)
- **18** Nonsense (5)
- **19** Author (8)

Down
- **2** Command (5)
- **3** Kevin ___ : former Australian Prime Minister (4)
- **4** You may have these while asleep (6)
- **5** Direct competitor (5)
- **6** First month (7)
- **8** Shuffle (7)
- **11** Moves smoothly (6)
- **13** Diving waterbird (5)
- **15** Ceases (5)
- **16** Skilfully; adeptly (4)

No. 205
Sunday July 24th 2022

Across

6 Perplexing situation (11)
7 Salad plant (5)
9 Decompose (5)
10 Nerve impulses (7)
13 Expressing emotions (of poetry) (5)
14 Spore-producing organisms (5)
15 Tree with distinctive bark (6,5)

Down

1 Glasses (abbrev.) (5)
2 Inevitably (11)
3 Shackle (8)
4 Opposing political progress (11)
5 Remains (5)
8 Sewed together (8)
11 Lavish (5)
12 Emits a breath of relief (5)

No. 206
Monday July 25th 2022

Across

3 Cooked slowly in liquid (6)
6 Walk heavily and firmly (5)
7 Final stage of an extended process (7)
9 Frenzied (5)
12 Plaintiff (11)
14 Place providing accommodation (5)
15 Illness (7)
17 Show triumphant joy (5)
18 Leased (6)

Down

1 Organ of digestion (7)
2 Large wine bottles (7)
3 Wonder about (9)
4 Swish (of an animal's tail) (3)
5 Dulls (4)
8 Very pleased (9)
10 Diplomatic (7)
11 Eg Usain Bolt (7)
13 Fibber (4)
16 Male person (3)

No. 207
Tuesday July 26th 2022

Across

1 Non-canonical religious texts (9)
6 Steep slope (5)
7 Nosed (anag) (5)
9 Bodyguards (7)
12 Film directed by Stephen Gaghan (7)
16 Rascal (5)
17 Large crow (5)
18 Believed (a lie) (9)

Down

2 Quartzlike gem (4)
3 Indian monetary unit (5)
4 Sudden fear (5)
5 Venomous snakes (6)
6 Husbands or wives (7)
8 Support or strengthen (7)
10 Violate a law of God (3)
11 Brief intervals (6)
13 First Greek letter (5)
14 Fourth month (5)
15 Affirm solemnly (4)

No. 208
Wednesday July 27th 2022

Across

1 Choosing to take up or follow (8)
6 Sturdy (5)
7 Raises up (5)
9 Remain or stay somewhere (4)
10 Have as a purpose (6)
12 Entry pass (6)
14 Correctional institution (4)
17 At that place; not here (5)
18 Receded (5)
19 Person who sees something (8)

Down

2 Challenged (5)
3 Yaps (anag) (4)
4 Doing nothing (6)
5 Blunder (5)
6 Natural environment (7)
8 Burdened (7)
11 Alcove (6)
13 Doctrine; system of beliefs (5)
15 Stroll (5)
16 Close by (4)

No. 209
Thursday July 28th 2022

Across

1 Endorsed (11)
7 Prepare for printing (7)
8 Expel (5)
9 Inexpensive (5)
11 State indirectly (5)
12 Area of open land (5)
13 Single-handed (7)
16 Not in the same way (11)

Down

1 Mud channel (3)
2 Container for a drink (3)
3 Make in bulk (4-7)
4 Destroy (11)
5 Bring to maturity (7)
6 Fate (7)
9 Pleased (7)
10 Become less intense (4,3)
14 Small spot (3)
15 Not wet (3)

No. 210
Friday July 29th 2022

Across

1 Deter (10)
5 Songbird (5)
7 Slender woman or girl (5)
9 Waste matter (6)
10 Persuade gently (4)
12 Solid; not soft (4)
13 Dock for small yachts (6)
16 Strain (5)
17 Anxiety (5)
18 Particularly (10)

Down

1 Deceives or misleads (5)
2 Interruption of service (6)
3 Prickly plant with fragrant flowers (4)
4 Running quickly (9)
6 Helpless (9)
8 Magic spell (3)
11 US state of islands (6)
12 Possesses (3)
14 Suitably (5)
15 Ewer (anag) (4)

No. 211
Saturday July 30th 2022

Across

1 Portable device to keep the rain off (8)
6 Impersonator (5)
7 Venomous snake (5)
9 Extinct bird (4)
10 Biochemical catalyst (6)
12 Surpass (6)
14 Capital of Norway (4)
17 Worthiness (5)
18 Work at a loom (5)
19 Deceptive (8)

Down

2 Conveyed by gestures (5)
3 Speed contest (4)
4 Shining with light (6)
5 Monastery church (5)
6 Trimmed (anag) (7)
8 Woodland plant (7)
11 Pertaining to the teeth (6)
13 Breed of dog (5)
15 Elevated step (5)
16 Inspires fear and wonder (4)

No. 212
Sunday July 31st 2022

Across

1 Parts that are left over (10)
5 Exit (5)
7 Welcome (5)
9 Silkworm covering (6)
10 Be suspended (4)
12 Tailless amphibian (4)
13 Part of the eye (6)
16 Musical instrument (5)
17 Genuflect (5)
18 Eg Shakespeare (10)

Down

1 Ancient object (5)
2 Refrigerator compartment (6)
3 Canines (4)
4 Test again (2-7)
6 Divine messenger (9)
8 Label (3)
11 Drinking container (6)
12 Also (3)
14 Dole out (5)
15 Feeling of resentment or jealousy (4)

No. 213
Monday August 1st 2022

Across
1 Decade from 1970 - 1979 (9)
6 Employer (5)
7 Deceives (5)
9 Thin and bony (7)
12 Whipping (7)
16 Spacious (5)
17 Sour substances (5)
18 Communication between minds (9)

Down
2 Action word (4)
3 Conventions (5)
4 Conclude; deduce (5)
5 Absorbent material (6)
6 Jumping athlete (7)
8 Cunning (7)
10 Metal container (3)
11 Classify (6)
13 Pastoral poem (5)
14 Seize firmly (5)
15 Reduce one's food intake (4)

No. 214
Tuesday August 2nd 2022

Across
2 Total weight of organisms (7)
6 Chances of winning (4)
9 Young bear (3)
10 Smart; chic (7)
11 Embodies (11)
12 Unfasten (7)
13 Annoy continuously (3)
14 Long poem (4)
15 Ennoble (7)

Down
1 Well-deserved fate (11)
3 Perform a religious ceremony (9)
4 High-ranking cleric (10)
5 Maintenance (11)
7 Very upset (10)
8 Flatterer (9)

No. 215
Wednesday August 3rd 2022

Across

1	Move from one system to another (6,4)
5	Delicious (5)
7	Sailing ship (5)
9	Highly motivated (6)
10	Confine; snare (4)
12	Indication (4)
13	Artificial waterways (6)
16	Loutish person (5)
17	Bright; cheery (5)
18	Good-looking (10)

Down

1	Quoted (5)
2	Hot spring (6)
3	Trees that bear acorns (4)
4	Amuse (9)
6	Catapult (9)
8	Fruit of a rose (3)
11	Unit of astronomical length (6)
12	Home for a pig (3)
14	Manner of writing (5)
15	Male hog (4)

No. 216
Thursday August 4th 2022

Across

2	Combustible (9)
7	Born (3)
8	Spirit of the time (9)
9	Mixing a deck of cards (9)
10	Feeling (9)
11	Attentiveness (9)
13	Bristle-like appendage (3)
14	Approximated (9)

Down

1	Examine in detail (11)
2	Flat-topped conical hat (3)
3	Forever (2,9)
4	Superb (11)
5	Come with (5)
6	Approximations (11)
10	Charming and endearing (5)
12	Sorrowful (3)

No. 217
Friday August 5th 2022

Across

1 Bacterial (anag) (9)
5 Catch or snare (6)
7 Type of high-energy radiation (1-3)
8 Hit with the fist (7)
11 First in importance (7)
14 Thin rope (4)
15 Roofing material made of straw (6)
16 Desire to set fire to things (9)

Down

1 Tidy (5,2)
2 Salad vegetable (7)
3 Poisonous (5)
4 Cabbagelike plant (4)
6 Judicious (7)
9 Cheer (7)
10 Former Greek monetary unit (7)
12 Violent disturbance (4)
13 Insanely (5)

No. 218
Saturday August 6th 2022

Across

1 Sparkling wine (4)
3 Launches on the stock market (6)
7 Obsession (5)
9 Up to the time when (5)
10 Information (7)
11 Charismatic person (7)
13 Constructed (5)
14 Make a god of (5)
15 Insanity (6)
16 Gelatinous substance (4)

Down

1 Temporary lodgings (5)
2 Exoneration (11)
4 Washed and ironed (9)
5 Amazing (11)
6 Vends (5)
8 Done spontaneously and without thought (9)
11 Inner circle (5)
12 Purchaser (5)

No. 219
Sunday August 7th 2022

Across

6 Large fruits with red pulp (11)
7 Data entered into a system (5)
9 Small woodland (5)
10 Opposite of shortest (7)
13 Despised (5)
14 Fight (3-2)
15 Positives and negatives (4,3,4)

Down

1 Expect to happen (5)
2 Condition in an agreement (11)
3 Educators (8)
4 Calculation (11)
5 Valuable thing (5)
8 Unable to appreciate music (4-4)
11 Hits with a lash (5)
12 Put out (5)

No. 220
Monday August 8th 2022

Across

1 Feeling resentment (9)
6 Country in South East Asia (5)
7 Departing (5)
9 Driven out (7)
12 Sudden increase (7)
16 Spiked weapon (5)
17 Accustom to something (5)
18 Sedimentary rock (9)

Down

2 Clothing (4)
3 Lacking meaning (5)
4 Not clearly stated (5)
5 Moves slowly and aimlessly (6)
6 Insects found where you sleep (7)
8 Resembling a deity (7)
10 Run steadily (3)
11 Rushes (anag) (6)
13 Broadcast again (5)
14 Leaves (5)
15 Popular martial art (4)

No. 221
Tuesday August 9th 2022

Across
1 Compassionate (11)
8 Become ready to eat (of fruit) (5)
9 Print anew (7)
10 Fantastically (11)
13 Senator (anag) (7)
14 Dried kernel of the coconut (5)
15 Energetically or vigorously (11)

Down
2 Movement (6)
3 From now on (9)
4 Recording medium (4)
5 Communicating (9)
6 Disadvantages (9)
7 Find out (9)
11 Opposite of winners (6)
12 Goad on (4)

No. 222
Wednesday August 10th 2022

Across
1 Unharmed (9)
5 Writhe (6)
7 Small mouse-like rodent (4)
8 Eternal (7)
11 Cause to deviate (7)
14 Long and limp (of hair) (4)
15 Greatly respect (6)
16 Moving staircase (9)

Down
1 Defective (7)
2 Stem the flow of (4,3)
3 Representative; messenger (5)
4 Large family (4)
6 Single eyeglass (7)
9 Vary the pitch of the voice (7)
10 Branch of linguistics (7)
12 School test (4)
13 Finds agreeable (5)

No. 223
Thursday August 11th 2022

Across

1 Individual; private (8)
6 Stable compartment (5)
7 Small branch (5)
9 Creative disciplines (4)
10 Huge desert in North Africa (6)
12 Tyrant (6)
14 After the beginning of (4)
17 Wall painting (5)
18 24th Greek letter (5)
19 In these times (8)

Down

2 Make law (5)
3 River sediment (4)
4 Capital of the Bahamas (6)
5 Insect grub (5)
6 Fame (7)
8 Kind of breakfast cereal (7)
11 Pursue (6)
13 Sound of an emergency vehicle (5)
15 Destitute (5)
16 Narrated (4)

No. 224
Friday August 12th 2022

Across

3 Hard tooth coating (6)
6 Excessively mean (5)
7 Cure-alls (7)
9 Good sense; reasoning (5)
12 Action of ending a partnership (11)
14 Oneness (5)
15 Obsequious person (7)
17 Pertaining to birds (5)
18 Thing that is totally true (6)

Down

1 Block (7)
2 Imply (7)
3 Let oracle (anag) (9)
4 Blend together (3)
5 Titled peer (4)
8 Initial (9)
10 Swimming costumes (7)
11 Undoing a knot (7)
13 Steep and rugged rock (4)
16 Used to be (3)

No. 225
Saturday August 13th 2022

Across
1 Residents (11)
7 Type of precision surgery (7)
8 Floral leaf (5)
9 Walk (5)
11 Collection of maps (5)
12 Searches for (5)
13 Part of a gun (7)
16 Dissatisfied (11)

Down
1 Annoy (3)
2 Animal fodder (3)
3 Company that transmits TV shows (11)
4 Feeling of fear (11)
5 Nasal opening (7)
6 Seafarers (7)
9 Binned (7)
10 People with detailed knowledge (7)
14 Leg (anag) (3)
15 Relieve or free from (3)

No. 226
Sunday August 14th 2022

Across
1 Reprimanding (7-3)
5 Competed in a speed contest (5)
7 Feign (5)
9 Sharpening (6)
10 Sharp bristle (4)
12 Charges (4)
13 Subject to a penalty (6)
16 Lighter (5)
17 District council head (5)
18 Having a favourable position (10)

Down
1 Portable source of light (5)
2 One of the halogens (6)
3 Desert in northern China (4)
4 Thrift (9)
6 Curdled (9)
8 Chain attached to a watch (3)
11 Surrender (6)
12 Dandy (3)
14 Biblical king (5)
15 Extent of a surface (4)

No. 227
Monday August 15th 2022

Across

2 European country (7)
5 Jostle and push (5)
6 Extremely cruel (7)
7 Edge or border (5)
10 Capturing interest (11)
12 Inert gas found in air (5)
13 Delightful (7)
14 Enumerates (5)
15 Improve (7)

Down

1 Willing to act dishonestly (7)
2 Torment or harass (7)
3 Increase in size (4)
4 State of the USA (8)
7 Grammatical case in Latin (8)
8 Shackle (7)
9 Repulsion (7)
11 Bone of the forearm (4)

No. 228
Tuesday August 16th 2022

Across

2 Refined; removed impurities (9)
7 Dove sound (3)
8 Athletic contest (9)
9 Very sensitive (of information) (3,6)
10 Given to using irony (9)
11 Mountain range in Italy (9)
13 Entirely (3)
14 Cosmetic product (9)

Down

1 Sparkle (11)
2 Cooking utensil (3)
3 Symbol of reconciliation (5,6)
4 Amused (11)
5 Break apart forcibly (5)
6 Energetically (11)
10 Type of leather (5)
12 Cutting tool (3)

No. 229
Wednesday August 17th 2022

Across

1 Ongoing television serial (4,5)
7 Sum charged (3)
8 Cutting; incisive (9)
9 Emoticons (anag) (9)
10 Protectors (9)
12 Applicable in all cases (9)
13 Long-leaved lettuce (3)
14 All people (9)

Down

1 Easy target (7,4)
2 ___ Adkins: singer (5)
3 Very happy (2,5,4)
4 Intricately (11)
5 Towards the stern (3)
6 Wonderfully (11)
11 US R&B singer (5)
12 Exploit unfairly (3)

No. 230
Thursday August 18th 2022

Across

2 Out of control (7)
5 Ruined; rendered inoperable (5)
6 Not modern (7)
7 Food blender (5)
10 Explanation of an event (11)
12 Remnant of a dying fire (5)
13 Reserved (7)
14 Outdoor shelters (5)
15 Keenly (7)

Down

1 Live together (7)
2 Listeners (7)
3 Defer action (4)
4 Form of make-up (8)
7 Drug that treats a disease (8)
8 More than enough (7)
9 Bows (7)
11 Release (4)

No. 231
Friday August 19th 2022

Across

1 Where something or someone originated (10)
5 Temporary police force (5)
7 Under (5)
9 Seaport in South Africa (6)
10 Incline (4)
12 Weds (anag) (4)
13 Arch of the foot (6)
16 Snarl (5)
17 Military trainee (5)
18 Person who makes iron goods (10)

Down

1 Animal that walks on two legs (5)
2 Doglike mammals (6)
3 Part of the ear (4)
4 Brought together (9)
6 Casual survey of opinion (5,4)
8 Came first in a race (3)
11 Bumps into (6)
12 Canine (3)
14 Business proposal (5)
15 ___ Stewart: ex-England cricketer (4)

No. 232
Saturday August 20th 2022

Across

6 A creative work such as a poem (11)
7 Up and about (5)
8 English royal house (5)
9 Shut in (7)
12 Lock of hair (5)
13 Pointed projectile (5)
14 Brevity in expressing oneself (11)

Down

1 Dispose of (5)
2 Small pieces (11)
3 Removes errors (8)
4 Of a generous disposition (4-7)
5 ___ Agassi: former tennis star (5)
8 Insincere and dishonest (3-5)
10 Block of wood (5)
11 Swill about (5)

No. 233
Sunday August 21st 2022

Across
2 Lay down in rest (7)
6 Hoodwink (4)
9 Haul (3)
10 Beat easily (7)
11 Narrator (11)
12 Affluent (7)
13 Sewn edge (3)
14 Lies (anag) (4)
15 Ebbs (7)

Down
1 Eg Plato (11)
3 Robber (9)
4 Moons (10)
5 Oppressed (11)
7 Enormous (10)
8 Person providing protection (9)

No. 234
Monday August 22nd 2022

Across
1 Record-keeping official (9)
6 Relinquish (5)
7 Titles (5)
9 Do away with (7)
12 Excuse (7)
16 Uncertainty (5)
17 Individual things (5)
18 Outstandingly bad (9)

Down
2 Female child (4)
3 Minute pore in a leaf (5)
4 Music with a recurrent theme (5)
5 Continue to exist (6)
6 Turned over; became very angry (7)
8 Learning institutions (7)
10 Container (3)
11 Reserved and coy (6)
13 Consumer of food (5)
14 Making a knot in (5)
15 Brave person; idol (4)

No. 235
Tuesday August 23rd 2022

Across

6 Past performances (5,6)
7 Slabs of peat for fuel (5)
9 Army rank (5)
10 Stopping place for a train (7)
13 Upper limits (5)
14 Indian lute (5)
15 Study of lawbreaking (11)

Down

1 Propose; utter (5)
2 Visible to the naked eye (11)
3 Mythical sea creatures (8)
4 Alignment of planets (11)
5 Decorate (5)
8 Spacecraft (8)
11 Area of land (5)
12 Becomes worn at the edges (5)

No. 236
Wednesday August 24th 2022

Across

2 Office (9)
7 Show discontent (3)
8 Obscure (9)
9 Necessary (9)
10 Irregular (9)
11 Excluding; alienating (9)
13 Possess (3)
14 Very sharp and perceptive (5-4)

Down

1 Causing a blockage (11)
2 Court (3)
3 Keep cold (11)
4 Thing that may happen (11)
5 Alert (5)
6 Attention-grabbing (3-8)
10 With a forward motion (5)
12 Superhuman being (3)

No. 237
Thursday August 25th 2022

Across

6 About to happen (11)
7 Fertile area in a desert (5)
9 Dreadful (5)
10 Less quiet (7)
13 Wanes (anag) (5)
14 A number between an eighth and a tenth (5)
15 Hostile and aggressive (11)

Down

1 Currently in progress (5)
2 Fit to be seen (11)
3 Symbols representing musical notes (8)
4 Dissimilarities (11)
5 Nimble (5)
8 Bathing costume (8)
11 Absorbent pads (5)
12 Closes (5)

No. 238
Friday August 26th 2022

Across

3 Gardening tool (6)
6 Lazy person; layabout (5)
7 Learning institution (7)
9 From the capital of Italy (5)
12 A law forbidding something (11)
14 Beneath (5)
15 Put in the ground (7)
17 Draw or bring out (5)
18 Tall castle structures (6)

Down

1 Play havoc with (7)
2 Confound (7)
3 Temporary (9)
4 Marry (3)
5 Luxurious car (abbrev.) (4)
8 Stances; ways of thinking (9)
10 Attentive; conscious of (7)
11 Twisted (of a tree) (7)
13 Overabundance (4)
16 At this moment (3)

No. 239
Saturday August 27th 2022

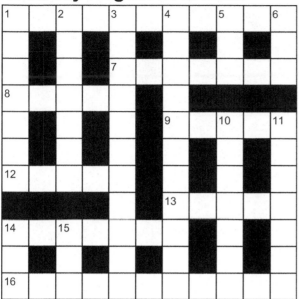

Across

1 Easily angered (3-8)
7 Absolutely incredible (7)
8 Small hill (5)
9 Golf clubs (5)
12 Mistaken (5)
13 Seasons (5)
14 Balearic Island (7)
16 Triangular pyramid (11)

Down

1 Item used to cut metal (7)
2 Capital of Ontario (7)
3 Desperate Housewives actress (3,8)
4 Cause to happen unexpectedly (11)
5 ___ Ferdinand: footballer (3)
6 Dr ___ : US rapper and record producer (3)
10 Located in the fresh air (7)
11 Official sitting (7)
14 Floor covering (3)
15 Extend out (3)

No. 240
Sunday August 28th 2022

Across

2 Tedium (7)
6 Killer whale (4)
9 Droop (3)
10 Series of boat races (7)
11 Formal declaration (11)
12 Sheer dress fabric (7)
13 Uncooked (of meat) (3)
14 List of food items available (4)
15 Most poorly lit (7)

Down

1 Of a cheerful disposition (4-7)
3 Self-control (9)
4 Remove salt from (10)
5 Generous (11)
7 Deep shade of blue (10)
8 Sum total (9)

No. 241
Monday August 29th 2022

Across

1 Sightings (8)
6 Service colour of the army (5)
7 Transparent solid (5)
9 ___ Ifans: Welsh actor (4)
10 Document fastener (6)
12 Get hold of (6)
14 Sued (anag) (4)
17 The beginning of an era (5)
18 Scent (5)
19 Window in a roof (8)

Down

2 Where one finds Rome (5)
3 Child who has no home (4)
4 Invalidate (6)
5 Skin on top of the head (5)
6 Form of singing for entertainment (7)
8 Slim (7)
11 Fourscore (6)
13 Runs at a moderate pace (5)
15 Apathy (5)
16 ___ Amos: US singer-songwriter (4)

No. 242
Tuesday August 30th 2022

Across

1 Vulnerable to (11)
8 Do extremely well at (5)
9 Feeling of indignation (7)
10 Compose a dance routine (11)
13 Business providing flights (7)
14 Drive forward (5)
15 Key details of a subject (5-6)

Down

2 Workplace for an artist (6)
3 Adolescents (9)
4 Opposite of front (4)
5 Illuminate (9)
6 Process of learning; schooling (9)
7 Usually (9)
11 Get off (6)
12 Facial blemish (4)

No. 243
Wednesday August 31st 2022

Across

1 Turn down (6)
4 Eg bullets (abbrev) (4)
7 ___ Ulvaeus: member of ABBA (5)
8 First appearance (5)
9 Trellis (anag) (7)
11 Brass wind instrument (7)
13 Sing like a bird (5)
14 Sweeping implement (5)
15 Toy for jumping about on (4)
16 Promotional material (6)

Down

1 Automaton (5)
2 Act of selling illegally (11)
3 End of a digit (9)
5 Portable communication device (6,5)
6 Denise van ___ : English actress (5)
8 Troubled (9)
10 Go over again (5)
12 Entice to do something (5)

No. 244
Thursday September 1st 2022

Across

1 Symmetrical open plane curve (8)
6 Skirmish (5)
7 Self-evident truth (5)
9 Topical information (4)
10 Naturally illuminated (6)
12 Building exhibiting objects (6)
14 Buckles (4)
17 Electronic device (5)
18 Loves uncritically (5)
19 Reading carefully (8)

Down

2 Permit (5)
3 Afresh (4)
4 Not allowing light to pass through (6)
5 A satellite of Uranus (5)
6 Smallest amount (7)
8 Type of cell division (7)
11 Writing desk (6)
13 Amazes (5)
15 Many times (5)
16 Anxious; nervous (4)

No. 245
Friday September 2nd 2022

Across

2 Wafer of semiconducting material used to make a circuit (9)
7 Sound that a cow makes (3)
8 Conduct legal proceedings against (9)
9 Cooking pots (9)
10 Type of pasta (9)
11 Failing to take proper care (9)
13 Belonging to us (3)
14 Exceedingly (9)

Down

1 Infinite knowledge (11)
2 Soak up; wipe away (3)
3 Business run jointly by its members (11)
4 Do better than expected (11)
5 Periods of 60 minutes (5)
6 Introductory (11)
10 Sense of seeing (5)
12 Plaything (3)

No. 246
Saturday September 3rd 2022

Across

1 One who does not eat meat (10)
5 Tall attractive flower (5)
7 One side of a gem (5)
9 Judged (6)
10 Body fat (4)
12 Reveal indiscreetly (4)
13 On ___ of: in the interests of (6)
16 Beast (5)
17 Vault under a church (5)
18 Translucent (3-7)

Down

1 Legally acceptable (5)
2 Coloured lightly (6)
3 A flat float (4)
4 Of secondary importance (9)
6 Too early (9)
8 Bat (anag) (3)
11 Swordsman (6)
12 Best ___ and tucker: smartest clothes (3)
14 Retrieve (5)
15 Immediately following (4)

No. 247
Sunday September 4th 2022

Across
1 Expulsion (8)
6 Diacritical mark (5)
7 Dance club (5)
9 Men (4)
10 Legal practitioner (6)
12 Take into the body (of food) (6)
14 Sudden desire (4)
17 Move effortlessly through air (5)
18 Protective garment worn in the kitchen (5)
19 Put at risk (8)

Down
2 Happy; jovial (5)
3 Cook (4)
4 Eg from New Delhi (6)
5 Beastly (5)
6 Labelling (7)
8 Rower (7)
11 Go up (6)
13 Assumed appearance (5)
15 Equine animal (5)
16 Near (anag) (4)

No. 248
Monday September 5th 2022

Across
1 Looked at open-mouthed (5)
5 Lover of Juliet (5)
6 Woody plant (4)
8 Regular salary (7)
10 Without giving a name (11)
11 Deciphering machine (7)
12 Cab (4)
14 Cooked in the oven (5)
15 Reverence for God (5)

Down
1 Stomach (3)
2 Easily achieved (5,2,4)
3 Mimic (11)
4 Word said on parting (7)
7 Speak haltingly (7)
9 Unrecoverable sum of money one is owed (3,4)
13 Climbing vine (3)

No. 249
Tuesday September 6th 2022

Across

2 Harsh; corrosive (7)
5 Mark of repetition (5)
6 Force of civilians trained as soldiers (7)
7 Parts (anag) (5)
10 Formal evening wear (6,5)
12 Position carefully (5)
13 The gathering of crops (7)
14 Praise highly (5)
15 Spun around (7)

Down

1 Putting away items (7)
2 Complicated (7)
3 Move in water (4)
4 Come together (8)
7 Small stall at a fair (8)
8 Formally approved (7)
9 Quick departure (7)
11 At any time (4)

No. 250
Wednesday September 7th 2022

Across

6 Community with a common interest (11)
7 Urns (5)
9 Engross oneself in (5)
10 Sustain with food (7)
13 Young boy or girl (5)
14 Loosely-woven cloth (5)
15 Eg Shakespeare and Bernard Shaw (11)

Down

1 Opposite of below (5)
2 Meaningless (11)
3 Urgent (8)
4 Consideration of the future (11)
5 Good at (5)
8 Closure of a system or factory (8)
11 Range (5)
12 Robbery (5)

No. 251
Thursday September 8th 2022

Across

1 Damage (a reputation) (8)
6 Lease (anag) (5)
7 Lift up (5)
9 Succulent (4)
10 Birthplace of St Francis (6)
12 Having only magnitude (of a quantity) (6)
14 Average value (4)
17 Flatten on impact (5)
18 Fault (5)
19 Wave or flourish in display (8)

Down

2 Gets less difficult (5)
3 Building for grinding grain (4)
4 Recycle old material (6)
5 Country once ruled by Papa Doc (5)
6 Signs up (7)
8 Narrower (7)
11 Frequently repeated phrase (6)
13 Speak without preparation (2-3)
15 Peers (5)
16 Transmit (4)

No. 252
Friday September 9th 2022

Across

3 Sloping (of a typeface) (6)
6 European country (5)
7 Mistake; blunder (4,3)
9 Attendant upon God (5)
12 Think about carefully (11)
14 Leaves out (5)
15 Makes unhappy (7)
17 All (5)
18 Legendary; mythical (6)

Down

1 With an attitude of suspicion (7)
2 Knocking loudly (7)
3 Have an effect on another (9)
4 Negligent (3)
5 Clothed (4)
8 Unchallenged (9)
10 Piece of furniture (7)
11 Jumpers (7)
13 One of two equal parts (4)
16 Small amount of something (3)

No. 253
Saturday September 10th 2022

Across

2 Caused by motion (7)
5 Angry dispute (3-2)
6 Unlawful (7)
7 Person who flies an aircraft (5)
10 Proficiently (11)
12 Work hard (5)
13 Release someone from duty (7)
14 Public disturbances (5)
15 Front runners (7)

Down

1 Catch fire (7)
2 Made a garment by intertwining threads (7)
3 Give out (4)
4 Substance that speeds up a reaction (8)
7 Pertaining to the chest (8)
8 Account books (7)
9 Type of alcohol (7)
11 Tie together (4)

No. 254
Sunday September 11th 2022

Across

1 Immensity (8)
6 Deep fissure (5)
7 One who makes bread (5)
9 Opposite of pull (4)
10 Glasses contain these (6)
12 Topics for debate (6)
14 Country in South America (4)
17 Donor (5)
18 Enclosed (of animals) (5)
19 Renovated (8)

Down

2 Approaches (5)
3 Raised edges (4)
4 Saturated (6)
5 Bonds of union (5)
6 Limiting (7)
8 Salvaged (7)
11 History play by Shakespeare (5,1)
13 Rescuer (5)
15 Large bird of prey (5)
16 Con; swindle (4)

No. 255
Monday September 12th 2022

Across
1 Not shortened (10)
5 Thick slices (5)
7 Besmirch (5)
9 Knocked gently (6)
10 Basic unit of matter (4)
12 Small metal spike (4)
13 Dribbles (6)
16 First Pope (5)
17 Enthusiasm (5)
18 Explorer (10)

Down
1 Surprise result (5)
2 Hurries (6)
3 Piece of office furniture (4)
4 Efforts (9)
6 Designated (of a time) (9)
8 Edge of a cup (3)
11 Radiating light; clever (6)
12 Quick sleep (3)
14 Search thoroughly for (5)
15 Spur on (4)

No. 256
Tuesday September 13th 2022

Across
2 Famous queen of Egypt (9)
7 Popular beverage (3)
8 Wok recipe (anag) (9)
9 Large bird (9)
10 Pertaining to the soul (9)
11 Reach a climax (9)
13 Piece of wood (3)
14 Biological community (9)

Down
1 Pain in a person's belly (7,4)
2 Close-fitting hat (3)
3 Form of energy (11)
4 Having greatest importance (11)
5 Eg screwdrivers and hammers (5)
6 Admit to be true (11)
10 Group of shots (5)
12 Tree of the genus Ulmus (3)

No. 257
Wednesday September 14th 2022

Across

2 Summary of events (5-2)
6 Abominable snowman (4)
9 17th Greek letter (3)
10 Slope (7)
11 General guideline (4,2,5)
12 Virtuoso solo passage (7)
13 Ate (anag) (3)
14 Touched (4)
15 Cunning (7)

Down

1 Devices popular before computers existed (11)
3 Inadvertent (9)
4 Remove restrictions from (10)
5 Chance of happening (11)
7 Make three copies of (10)
8 Agreeing (9)

No. 258
Thursday September 15th 2022

Across

2 Country in Central America (9)
7 Sticky substance (3)
8 Persistent and dogged (9)
9 Letters are put in these (9)
10 Exercise of absolute power (9)
11 Ornate (9)
13 Lipid (3)
14 Growing old (9)

Down

1 Eternity (11)
2 Word expressing negation (3)
3 Decisions reached by reasoning (11)
4 Give in return (11)
5 Merchandise; possessions (5)
6 Homework tasks (11)
10 Draw off liquid from (5)
12 Young newt (3)

No. 259
Friday September 16th 2022

Across

1 Learned people (8)
6 Cry of excitement (5)
7 ___ Tuck: friend of Robin Hood (5)
9 ___ Kournikova: former tennis star (4)
10 Characteristically French (6)
12 Pieces of writing (6)
14 Hens lay these (4)
17 Store in a secret place (5)
18 Baking appliances (5)
19 Solitary (8)

Down

2 Children's entertainer (5)
3 Exclamation on making a mistake (4)
4 Disturbance (6)
5 Ability (5)
6 Ferocious small mammals (7)
8 Actress (anag) (7)
11 Punctuation mark (6)
13 Pashmina (5)
15 Shine brightly (5)
16 Dove sounds (4)

No. 260
Saturday September 17th 2022

Across

1 Stream or small river (4)
3 Required (6)
7 Stringed instruments (5)
9 Takes a break (5)
10 Irreverence (7)
11 Character in Hamlet (7)
13 Charming and elegant (5)
14 Gaze fixedly (5)
15 Tropical fly (6)
16 Areas of ground for growing plants (4)

Down

1 Pleasantly warm (of weather) (5)
2 Well-known sentence (11)
4 Eg natives of France and Germany (9)
5 Scatter widely (11)
6 Study (anag) (5)
8 Calmness (9)
11 The beginning of something (5)
12 Experiences through touch (5)

133

No. 261
Sunday September 18th 2022

Across
- **2** Vain (9)
- **7** Pen point (3)
- **8** Large body of troops (9)
- **9** Kinsfolk (9)
- **10** Greatly respected (9)
- **11** Merchants who sell goods (9)
- **13** Having a high temperature (3)
- **14** Lively (9)

Down
- **1** Gives extra weight to (11)
- **2** Decline (3)
- **3** Amazingly good (11)
- **4** Unintentional (11)
- **5** Two children born at the same time (5)
- **6** Accomplice (11)
- **10** Elector (5)
- **12** Introverted (3)

No. 262
Monday September 19th 2022

Across
- **1** A periodical that is usually daily (9)
- **6** Shared by two or more people (5)
- **7** Satiates (5)
- **9** Small bone in the ear (7)
- **12** Root vegetables (7)
- **16** Noble gas (5)
- **17** Belonging to them (5)
- **18** Delight beyond measure (9)

Down
- **2** Cry with sorrow or grief (4)
- **3** Paved courtyard (5)
- **4** Swells (5)
- **5** Artefacts (6)
- **6** Largest planet (7)
- **8** More sugary (7)
- **10** Asp (anag) (3)
- **11** Horse restraint (6)
- **13** Interior (5)
- **14** Scheme intended to deceive (3-2)
- **15** Domesticated ox (4)

No. 263
Tuesday September 20th 2022

Across

1 Type of postage stamp (6-5)
7 Imprecise (7)
8 Quavering sound (5)
9 Store of hoarded wealth (5)
12 Vertical part of a step (5)
13 Deciduous coniferous tree (5)
14 Mound made by insects (7)
16 Cooking utensils (11)

Down

1 Window panel for keeping light out (7)
2 Gambling houses (7)
3 Cosmetic lacquer (4,7)
4 Dejected (11)
5 Military commander or official (3)
6 Drunkard (3)
10 Musical wind instrument (7)
11 Speak excitedly of (7)
14 Seabird (3)
15 Blue ___ : bird (3)

No. 264
Wednesday September 21st 2022

Across

2 Achieved a goal (9)
7 How (anag) (3)
8 Female ballet dancer (9)
9 Made short and sharp turns (9)
10 Forecast (9)
11 Attractive (9)
13 Curved shape (3)
14 Pushed down (9)

Down

1 European country (11)
2 Cry (3)
3 Work together (11)
4 Crises (11)
5 Removed water (5)
6 Fault-finding programs (11)
10 Appear suddenly (3,2)
12 Gallivant (3)

135

No. 265
Thursday September 22nd 2022

Across
1 Act of saying farewell (11)
8 Creator (5)
9 Soft metallic element (7)
10 Restraint (4-7)
13 Raises (7)
14 Higher in place (5)
15 Parakeets (11)

Down
2 Edible pulse (6)
3 Blend (9)
4 Sink (anag) (4)
5 Confident (9)
6 Source of a brief burst of bright light (9)
7 Converse (9)
11 A palm tree (6)
12 Familiar name for a potato (4)

No. 266
Friday September 23rd 2022

Across
6 Large and heavy vehicles (11)
7 Remains; destroys (5)
9 Lentil or chickpea (5)
10 Pompous person (7)
13 Supple (5)
14 Destiny; fate (5)
15 Praiseworthy (11)

Down
1 Narrow sea inlet (5)
2 Science of farming (11)
3 Type of bag (8)
4 Impenetrable (11)
5 Trees (anag) (5)
8 Believes tentatively (8)
11 Fall heavily (5)
12 Impudent; full of spirit (5)

No. 267
Saturday September 24th 2022

Across
1 Expects to happen (11)
7 Sailor (7)
8 Academy Award (5)
9 Game of chance (5)
11 Flexible insulated cables (5)
12 Prevent (5)
13 Plants that live a year or less (7)
16 Virtually (11)

Down
1 Goal (3)
2 Bitumen (3)
3 Naturally associated (11)
4 Relating to fireworks (11)
5 Instructor (7)
6 Origins (7)
9 Disperse (5,2)
10 Short story (7)
14 Trouble in body or mind (3)
15 Secret agent (3)

No. 268
Sunday September 25th 2022

Across
2 Request earnestly (7)
5 Type of coffee drink (5)
6 Smoothing clothes (7)
7 Ethical (5)
10 Interference (11)
12 Stitched (5)
13 Brings about (7)
14 Arose from slumber (5)
15 Plunder (7)

Down
1 Female stage performer (7)
2 Withdraw from a commitment (4,3)
3 Sea eagle (4)
4 Large cask (8)
7 Changed (8)
8 At the ocean floor (7)
9 Technical knowledge (4-3)
11 Rounded protuberance on a camel (4)

No. 269
Monday September 26th 2022

Across

1 Examples (9)
6 Very large (5)
7 Loop with a running knot (5)
9 Quantities (7)
12 Corridor (7)
16 Special reward (5)
17 Borders (5)
18 Farm machines (9)

Down

2 Identical; unchanged (4)
3 Hawaiian greeting (5)
4 Showing a willingness to achieve results (3-2)
5 Faints (6)
6 Top prize (7)
8 Military flags (7)
10 Periodic publication (abbrev.) (3)
11 Feature (6)
13 Change (5)
14 Levels out (5)
15 Look at amorously (4)

No. 270
Tuesday September 27th 2022

Across

1 Free from control (11)
7 Expressing boredom with the mouth (7)
8 U-shaped curve in a river (5)
9 Ruin (5)
11 Tree of the birch family (5)
12 Faint bird cry (5)
13 Statement of commemoration (7)
16 Oversee (11)

Down

1 Very cold; slippery (3)
2 Ground condensation (3)
3 Spiny cactus fruit (7,4)
4 Discussion aimed at reaching an agreement (11)
5 Helped to happen (7)
6 Fishing boat (7)
9 Observes (7)
10 Surround entirely (7)
14 Affirmative vote (3)
15 Possessed (3)

No. 271
Wednesday September 28th 2022

Across

2 Piece of cloth that covers the eyes (9)
7 Long and narrow inlet (3)
8 Malevolence (9)
9 Settle an argument (9)
10 Not embarrassed (9)
11 Conjuring up a picture of (9)
13 Pot (3)
14 Urgent crisis (9)

Down

1 Happening in stages (11)
2 Disallow (3)
3 Suggesting indirectly (11)
4 Apotheosis (11)
5 Corpulent (5)
6 Insubordinate (11)
10 Customary practice (5)
12 A man; fellow (3)

No. 272
Thursday September 29th 2022

Across

1 Not moving (10)
5 Tiny piece of food (5)
7 Student (5)
9 Person who copies out documents (6)
10 In a lazy way (4)
12 Married woman (4)
13 Dishes of leafy greens (6)
16 Uptight (5)
17 Representative (5)
18 Reprimand (10)

Down

1 Draws into the mouth (5)
2 Drink (6)
3 Back of the neck (4)
4 Reject (9)
6 Coarse (9)
8 Put down (3)
11 Highly seasoned type of sausage (6)
12 Damp (3)
14 Silk fabric (5)
15 Pose (anag) (4)

No. 273
Friday September 30th 2022

Across

1 Trade title of a product (5,4)
5 Where one finds Quebec (6)
7 Unit of heredity (4)
8 Spread widely (7)
11 Constantly present (7)
14 Successful move (4)
15 Pertaining to a nerve (6)
16 Something that is revealing (3-6)

Down

1 Due to the fact that (7)
2 Segmented worm (7)
3 Strength (5)
4 Poker stake (4)
6 Caution (anag) (7)
9 Type of monkey (7)
10 Walker without a fixed route (7)
12 Cranny (4)
13 Not containing anything (5)

No. 274
Saturday October 1st 2022

Across

3 Wonder at (6)
6 One of the United Arab Emirates (5)
7 Ordering (7)
9 Ticked over (of an engine) (5)
12 Device used to increase thrust (11)
14 Exposed (5)
15 Male chicken (7)
17 Opposite of a winner (5)
18 State of great comfort (6)

Down

1 Commander in chief of a fleet (7)
2 Aptitude (7)
3 Send to the wrong place (9)
4 Vessel (3)
5 Solitary (4)
8 Frequently (9)
10 Put in someone's care (7)
11 Starred (anag) (7)
13 Loose hood (4)
16 One more than five (3)

No. 275
Sunday October 2nd 2022

Across

1 Not alike (10)
6 Tina (anag) (4)
7 Split along a natural line (6)
8 Title placed before a name (6)
9 Knuckle of pork (4)
11 Egyptian goddess (4)
13 Concerned with sight (6)
15 Action of making use of something (6)
17 Extreme point (4)
18 Of external origin (10)

Down

2 Entrails (7)
3 Breathe in audibly (5)
4 Annelid worm with suckers (5)
5 Increase the running speed of an engine (3)
7 Person who steers a boat (3)
10 Country house (7)
12 Set out (5)
13 Compete for (3)
14 Stagnant (5)
16 Type of statistical chart (3)

No. 276
Monday October 3rd 2022

Across

1 Study of earthquakes (10)
5 Country whose capital is Tripoli (5)
7 Exclusive story (5)
9 Snarls (6)
10 Summit of a small hill (4)
12 24-hour periods (4)
13 Changes; differs (6)
16 Compassion (5)
17 Cylinder of smoking tobacco (5)
18 Punctuation mark (10)

Down

1 Seals (anag) (5)
2 Nastily (6)
3 Whip (4)
4 Basic training (9)
6 Snare set as a practical joke (5,4)
8 Fizzy drink (3)
11 Eg Darcey Bussell (6)
12 Water barrier (3)
14 Bout of extravagant shopping (5)
15 Fitness centres (4)

No. 277
Tuesday October 4th 2022

Across

1 Excessively talkative (9)
5 Take as being true (6)
7 Donkey noise (4)
8 Of great size (7)
11 Cigar (7)
14 Pottery material (4)
15 Large birds of prey (6)
16 Brought to a destination (9)

Down

1 Vivid (7)
2 Laughable (7)
3 Shadow (5)
4 Indian garment (4)
6 Perfect example of a quality (7)
9 Tool for cutting metal (7)
10 Flowed (of liquid) (7)
12 Clutched (4)
13 Poetic verse (5)

No. 278
Wednesday October 5th 2022

Across

1 Female officer of the law (11)
7 Affably (7)
8 Scale representation (5)
9 ___ Dushku: True Lies actress (5)
12 Mortise partner (5)
13 Metric unit of capacity (5)
14 Sporting dog (7)
16 Overstated (11)

Down

1 Remittance (7)
2 Give up or surrender something (3,4)
3 Questioning a statement (11)
4 Pertaining to office workers (5-6)
5 Queen ___ : fairy in Romeo and Juliet (3)
6 Negative vote (3)
10 A precise point in time (7)
11 Changed (7)
14 Perceive with the eyes (3)
15 ___ Ivanovic: tennis star (3)

No. 279
Thursday October 6th 2022

Across

2 Fabric (7)
6 Destroy (4)
9 Male offspring (3)
10 Period of prolonged dryness (7)
11 Speculative (11)
12 Cherubic (7)
13 Research place (abbrev.) (3)
14 Coalition of countries (4)
15 Slandered (7)

Down

1 Missiles (11)
3 Disobediently (9)
4 Belonging to the past (10)
5 Temporary inability to remember something (6,5)
7 Incontestable (10)
8 Person from another country (9)

No. 280
Friday October 7th 2022

Across

1 David ____ : novel by Charles Dickens (11)
7 Flightless seabird (7)
8 Totem (anag) (5)
9 Disgust (5)
12 New ____ : Indian capital (5)
13 Ben ____ : Scottish mountain (5)
14 Fail to repay a loan (7)
16 Act of hiding something (11)

Down

1 Order (7)
2 Incomplete (7)
3 Money spent (11)
4 Basic (11)
5 ____ de Cologne: perfume (3)
6 Greyish-brown colour (3)
10 Personal (7)
11 Civil action brought to court (7)
14 Ant and ____ : TV presenters (3)
15 Fish appendage (3)

No. 281
Saturday October 8th 2022

Across
1 Vanished (11)
7 Digit (7)
8 Form of expression (5)
9 Water container (5)
11 Teacher (5)
12 Train tracks (5)
13 Small amount (7)
16 In a state of disrepair (11)

Down
1 Secret retreat (3)
2 Add together (3)
3 Joint business (11)
4 Educated (11)
5 Shining (7)
6 Percussion musician (7)
9 Having facial hair (7)
10 Uncomplaining (7)
14 In good health (3)
15 Protective cover (3)

No. 282
Sunday October 9th 2022

Across
1 Advocate of private ownership (10)
5 Ladies (5)
7 Pointed; acute (5)
9 Smelling horrible (of old food) (6)
10 Bypass (4)
12 Shine (4)
13 Duty or tax (6)
16 Adhesive (5)
17 Roman cloaks (5)
18 Similarly (10)

Down
1 Crouch down in fear (5)
2 Substance found in wine (6)
3 Opposite of win (4)
4 Fizzing (9)
6 Public declaration of policy (9)
8 Liveliness (3)
11 Threat (anag) (6)
12 Dance (3)
14 Hard to please (5)
15 Vehicle with four-wheel drive (4)

No. 283
Monday October 10th 2022

Across

6 Curse (11)
7 Fastening device (5)
8 Old-fashioned (5)
9 Impresario (7)
12 Large amounts of land (5)
13 A fact that has been verified (5)
14 Glass buildings (11)

Down

1 Loose overall (5)
2 Byword for the British Press (5,6)
3 Versions of a book (8)
4 Recognise as different (11)
5 Positive electrode (5)
8 Opposite of a promotion (8)
10 Suspends (5)
11 Selected (5)

No. 284
Tuesday October 11th 2022

Across

6 Traitorous (11)
7 Bungle (5)
9 Ravine (5)
10 Revoke (7)
13 Divide in two (5)
14 Mexican plant fibre (5)
15 Upsetting (11)

Down

1 Cigarette ends (5)
2 Lacking distinguishing characteristics (11)
3 Flightless seabirds (8)
4 Camaraderie (11)
5 Tiles (anag) (5)
8 Inn (8)
11 Disreputable (5)
12 Blocks a hole (5)

No. 285
Wednesday October 12th 2022

Across

1 Having a widespread range (3-8)
7 Increases a deadline (7)
8 Indifferent to emotions (5)
9 ___ Federer: tennis star (5)
12 Quantitative relation between two amounts (5)
13 Green citrus fruits (5)
14 Pertaining to marriage (7)
16 Large car windows (11)

Down

1 Make agitated; unsettle (7)
2 Narrate (7)
3 Branch of physics (11)
4 Larva of a butterfly (11)
5 ___ Botham: cricketer (3)
6 State of matter (3)
10 Quick look (7)
11 Explanations (7)
14 Of recent origin (3)
15 Animal enclosure (3)

No. 286
Thursday October 13th 2022

Across

2 Marched in a formal procession (7)
6 Ill-mannered (4)
9 Tack (3)
10 Aseptic (7)
11 Enthusiastic supporter (11)
12 Large web-footed bird (7)
13 Female kangaroo (3)
14 True and actual (4)
15 Diminish the worth of (7)

Down

1 Taped in advance (3-8)
3 Home (9)
4 State of reliance (10)
5 Perilously (11)
7 Lack of courtesy (10)
8 Intense type of pain (9)

No. 287
Friday October 14th 2022

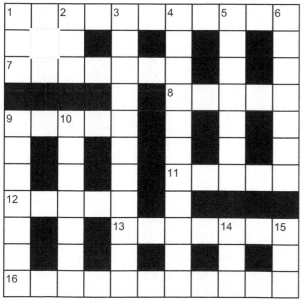

Across
1 Strong type of coffee (8)
6 Media (anag) (5)
7 Japanese poem (5)
9 Performs on stage (4)
10 Make better (6)
12 Positioned in the middle (6)
14 Splendid display and ceremony (4)
17 Male duck (5)
18 Enlighten; educate morally (5)
19 Hand-woven pictorial design (8)

Down
2 Garment with sleeves (5)
3 Long grass (4)
4 Winged monster of Thebes (6)
5 Small antelope (5)
6 Shocked (7)
8 Sad (7)
11 Fictional (4,2)
13 Early version of a document (5)
15 Willow twig (5)
16 Clarets (4)

No. 288
Saturday October 15th 2022

Across
1 Tolerant in one's views (5-6)
7 Obedient (7)
8 Unfasten (5)
9 Fantastic (5)
11 Unpleasant giants (5)
12 Bolt for fastening metal plates (5)
13 Copy; mimic (7)
16 Type of triangle (11)

Down
1 Flower that is not yet open (3)
2 Opposite of in (3)
3 Respectful (11)
4 Type of magician (11)
5 Feel very down (7)
6 Main meals (7)
9 Surprise (7)
10 Upstart; one who has recently gained wealth (7)
14 Mixture of gases we breathe (3)
15 Snake-like fish (3)

No. 289
Sunday October 16th 2022

Across

1 Gradual increase in loudness (9)
6 Prayers (5)
7 Grade (anag) (5)
9 Severely (7)
12 River of South East Africa (7)
16 Short choral composition (5)
17 Irritates (5)
18 Scheme (9)

Down

2 Days before major events (4)
3 Bags (5)
4 Courage; boldness (5)
5 Church instruments (6)
6 Dilemma (7)
8 Aridity (7)
10 Helpful hint (3)
11 Strikes firmly (6)
13 External (5)
14 Should (5)
15 Shoe with a wooden sole (4)

No. 290
Monday October 17th 2022

Across

1 Scary movie (6,4)
5 Burrowing animals (5)
7 Part of the hand (5)
9 Bright patch of colour (6)
10 Participate in a game (4)
12 Frozen rain (4)
13 Jumped up (6)
16 Plant flower (5)
17 Astonish (5)
18 Severe in manner (10)

Down

1 Rounded protuberances on camels (5)
2 Be preoccupied with something (6)
3 Fundraising party (4)
4 Capital of Slovenia (9)
6 Sweets on sticks (9)
8 Purchase (3)
11 Wrench an ankle (6)
12 Centre of activity (3)
14 Big (5)
15 ___ Sharif: Egyptian actor (4)

No. 291
Tuesday October 18th 2022

Across

2 Naval officer (9)
7 19th Greek letter (3)
8 Groups of three books (9)
9 Card game for one (9)
10 Slender flexible squid appendages (9)
11 Prompting (9)
13 Lubricate (3)
14 Tightly bound together (5-4)

Down

1 Creating an evocative mood (11)
2 Snip (3)
3 Upkeep (11)
4 Feeling of hatred (11)
5 Operate a motor vehicle (5)
6 Trustworthy (11)
10 Speed music is played at (5)
12 Obtained (3)

No. 292
Wednesday October 19th 2022

Across

1 Resort in Monaco (5,5)
6 Sixth Greek letter (4)
7 Recreate (6)
8 Although (6)
9 Three feet length (4)
11 Quantity of paper (4)
13 In slow time (of music) (6)
15 Abandon a plan (6)
17 Double-reed instrument (4)
18 Corporations (10)

Down

2 Position on top of (7)
3 Commerce (5)
4 Card game (5)
5 Tree that bears acorns (3)
7 Rodent (3)
10 Horizontal plant stem (7)
12 Grinding machines (5)
13 Wonder (3)
14 Basic units of an element (5)
16 Cooking appliance (3)

No. 293
Thursday October 20th 2022

Across

2 Occurs (7)
5 Wireless (5)
6 Greek white wine (7)
7 A written document (5)
10 Not achieving the desired result (11)
12 Looks slyly (5)
13 Spiny anteater (7)
14 Relation by marriage (2-3)
15 Chemical element with symbol Y (7)

Down

1 Modified (7)
2 Shock greatly (7)
3 Annoying person (4)
4 State of total disorder (8)
7 Lavish (8)
8 Praise enthusiastically (7)
9 Softly; not loudly (7)
11 Platform leading out to sea (4)

No. 294
Friday October 21st 2022

Across

3 Involuntary spasm (6)
6 Puny (5)
7 Honesty; integrity (7)
9 Rope with a running noose (5)
12 Milieu (11)
14 Flaring stars (5)
15 Large marine algae (7)
17 Finished (5)
18 Had corresponding sounds (6)

Down

1 Rinsed around (7)
2 Wistfully thoughtful (7)
3 Their copy (anag) (9)
4 Taxi (3)
5 Golf stroke on the green (4)
8 Without fixed limits (4-5)
10 Spread throughout (7)
11 Is present at (7)
13 Change direction suddenly (4)
16 Method; road (3)

No. 295
Saturday October 22nd 2022

Across
1 Of like kind (4)
3 Smear or blur (6)
7 Type of plastic (5)
9 Male monarchs (5)
10 Wicked act (7)
11 Italian red wine (7)
13 Japanese form of fencing (5)
14 Delay or linger (5)
15 Lasted (anag) (6)
16 Ancient harp (4)

Down
1 Rescued (5)
2 Not absolute (11)
4 Temporary (9)
5 Type of social occasion (6,5)
6 Became less difficult (5)
8 Flatfish of the plaice family (5,4)
11 Baked sweet treats (5)
12 Perhaps (5)

No. 296
Sunday October 23rd 2022

Across
1 Leaving out (8)
6 Verbose (5)
7 Spore (anag) (5)
9 Small bottle (4)
10 Unmoving (6)
12 Immature insects (6)
14 High-value playing cards (4)
17 Agree or correspond (5)
18 Functions correctly (5)
19 Scatter in drops (8)

Down
2 ___ Sharapova: tennis player (5)
3 Playthings (4)
4 Attribute to (6)
5 Phantasm (5)
6 Ripple on water (7)
8 Forgives for a fault (7)
11 Woodcutter (6)
13 Parts in a play (5)
15 Pinkish-red colour (5)
16 Clive ___ : British Sin City actor (4)

No. 297
Monday October 24th 2022

Across

6 Cheap accommodation provider (5,6)
7 Mature person (5)
8 Make an earnest appeal (5)
9 Restrain (7)
12 Religious doctrine (5)
13 Prologue (abbrev) (5)
14 Smooth and musical (of a sound) (11)

Down

1 Minor road (5)
2 In an abundant and lush manner (11)
3 Gossip (4-4)
4 Testimony (11)
5 A clearing in a wood (5)
8 Not privately (8)
10 Impress a pattern on (5)
11 Awaken (5)

No. 298
Tuesday October 25th 2022

Across

2 Choice (9)
7 Ancient boat (3)
8 Forbid (9)
9 Study of the origins of the universe (9)
10 Assessment or evaluation (9)
11 False opinion (9)
13 Increase in amount (3)
14 Disapproved of vehemently (9)

Down

1 Causing sudden upheaval (11)
2 Snow runner (3)
3 Outer part of the earth (11)
4 Company (11)
5 Frostily (5)
6 Holland (11)
10 Crime of burning something (5)
12 Craze (3)

No. 299
Wednesday October 26th 2022

Across

2 Inflexible and unyielding (7)
5 Muscular contraction (5)
6 Precondition (7)
7 Bore into (5)
10 Having power (11)
12 Floating platforms (5)
13 Faithfulness (7)
14 Golf shots (5)
15 Thaw (7)

Down

1 Duties or taxes (7)
2 Clap (7)
3 Relocate (4)
4 Bothers (8)
7 Rained gently (8)
8 Encode (7)
9 Outsiders (7)
11 Just and unbiased (4)

No. 300
Thursday October 27th 2022

Across

1 Word used by magicians (11)
8 Cut back a tree (5)
9 Tallier (anag) (7)
10 Dignified manner or conduct (11)
13 Passionate (7)
14 Precise (5)
15 Item that measures temperature (11)

Down

2 Sense of musical time (6)
3 Act of using up resources (9)
4 Boxing match (4)
5 Useful facilities (9)
6 Karate expert (5,4)
7 Botanical garden for trees (9)
11 Evoke (6)
12 Long flowing hair (4)

No. 301
Friday October 28th 2022

Across

1 Bucket (4)
3 Parcel (anag) (6)
7 Topic (anag) (5)
9 Gets larger (5)
10 Game where success is based on luck (7)
11 Type of deer (7)
13 Ray (5)
14 Overcooked (5)
15 Complied with a command (6)
16 Smudge (4)

Down

1 Explore or examine (5)
2 Unwillingness to accept the views of others (11)
4 Incandescent lamp (9)
5 Type of fat (11)
6 Harsh and grating in sound (5)
8 Perform a religious ceremony (9)
11 Brief appearance (5)
12 Religious table (5)

No. 302
Saturday October 29th 2022

Across

3 Raised (6)
6 Smooth cream of vegetables (5)
7 Imitator (7)
9 Small marine fish (5)
12 Becoming less (11)
14 Country in the Himalayas (5)
15 Topic (7)
17 Turn inside out (5)
18 Mocked (6)

Down

1 One event in a sequence (7)
2 Ancient warship (7)
3 Shape with four straight sides (9)
4 Beam of light (3)
5 Fine powder (4)
8 Fronted a TV show (9)
10 Spots (7)
11 Nimbleness (7)
13 Contented cat sound (4)
16 Sharp blow (3)

No. 303
Sunday October 30th 2022

Across
2 Decreased (7)
6 Word that identifies a thing (4)
9 Strong drink (3)
10 Played out (7)
11 Journeys of exploration (11)
12 Rattling noise (7)
13 Nevertheless (3)
14 Small flake of soot (4)
15 Puts up with (7)

Down
1 Unbearable (11)
3 Penniless (9)
4 Record of heart activity (10)
5 Show (11)
7 Unforeseen (10)
8 Abrasive used for smoothing (9)

No. 304
Monday October 31st 2022

Across
1 Cramped (8)
6 Move quickly (5)
7 Savoury meat jelly (5)
9 Pulls at (4)
10 Participant in a game (6)
12 Make less dense (6)
14 Very short skirt or dress (4)
17 Eg mallards (5)
18 Wide (5)
19 Intrigue (8)

Down
2 Outstanding (of a debt) (5)
3 Frizzy mass of hair (4)
4 Almost (6)
5 Idiotic (5)
6 Irrigated (7)
8 Transported by hand (7)
11 Compensate for (6)
13 Christina ___ : Addams Family actress (5)
15 People who are greatly admired (5)
16 Seal of the Archbishop of York (4)

No. 305
Tuesday November 1st 2022

Across

6 Division into two branches (11)
7 Former name of the Democratic Republic of Congo (5)
9 Inactive (5)
10 Make damp (7)
13 Tiny arachnids (5)
14 Put off (5)
15 Supreme authority (11)

Down

1 Humming (5)
2 Agreeing with a request (11)
3 Fed to completeness (8)
4 Sleeping through winter (11)
5 Midges (5)
8 Person sent on a special mission (8)
11 Accumulate (5)
12 Horse carts (5)

No. 306
Wednesday November 2nd 2022

Across

2 Hide (7)
6 Solemn promise (4)
9 Self-esteem (3)
10 Identifying outfit (7)
11 Utility (11)
12 The small details of something (7)
13 Owed and payable (3)
14 Computer memory unit (4)
15 Beg (7)

Down

1 Pamper (11)
3 Disrepute (9)
4 Simple (10)
5 Brave (11)
7 Competition (10)
8 Sleep through winter (9)

No. 307
Thursday November 3rd 2022

Across
1 Guidance; direction (10)
6 Girl's toy (4)
7 Sausage in a roll (3,3)
8 Liquid container (6)
9 Conceal (4)
11 For Your ___ Only: Bond film (4)
13 City in NE Italy (6)
15 Descend down a cliff (6)
17 Mud (4)
18 Pen name (3,2,5)

Down
2 Branch of biology (7)
3 Glazed earthenware (5)
4 Emerge from an egg (5)
5 In favour of (3)
7 Weeding tool (3)
10 Dignified conduct (7)
12 Water vapour (5)
13 ___ Kilmer: famous actor (3)
14 Rafael ___ : Spanish tennis star (5)
16 Rubbish holder (3)

No. 308
Friday November 4th 2022

Across
1 Relation by marriage (6-2-3)
7 Not in a hurry (7)
8 Feudal vassal (5)
9 Large indefinite quantities (5)
12 Produce a literary work (5)
13 Remorse (5)
14 Flamboyant confidence of style (7)
16 Act of looking after children (11)

Down
1 Swift-flying songbird (7)
2 Light compositions (7)
3 Things that happen to you (11)
4 Clever (11)
5 Strong alkaline solution (3)
6 Intelligence; humour (3)
10 Relating to knowledge based on deduction (1,6)
11 Solidifying (7)
14 Tavern (3)
15 The gist of the matter (3)

No. 309
Saturday November 5th 2022

Across
6 Greenish (11)
7 Passenger ship (5)
8 Bob ___ : US singer (5)
9 Import barrier (7)
12 Pass a rope through (5)
13 Destroy (3,2)
14 Changed completely (11)

Down
1 Ellipses (5)
2 Award for third place (6,5)
3 Extremely lovable (8)
4 Flared trousers (4-7)
5 Trick or feat of daring (5)
8 Eg Baz Luhrmann (8)
10 Scamps (5)
11 Potatoes (informal) (5)

No. 310
Sunday November 6th 2022

Across
1 Insults (11)
7 Mental process or idea (7)
8 Acoustic detection system (5)
9 Beer (5)
12 Stringed instrument (5)
13 Supplementary component (3-2)
14 One who performs duties for another (7)
16 Advertisements (11)

Down
1 Severe (7)
2 Thing causing outrage (7)
3 Extend by inference (11)
4 Posing a difficulty (11)
5 Toothed wheel (3)
6 Become firm (3)
10 Venetian boat (7)
11 Symptom of blushing (7)
14 Pouch; enclosed space (3)
15 Male sheep (3)

No. 311
Monday November 7th 2022

Across

1 Course for horse racing (9)
6 Torn apart (5)
7 Embed; type of filling (5)
9 Plot (7)
12 US space probe to Jupiter (7)
16 Sea duck (5)
17 Moist (of air) (5)
18 Cherishes as sacred (9)

Down

2 Guinea pig (4)
3 Cloak (5)
4 Extraterrestrial (5)
5 SI unit of thermodynamic temperature (6)
6 Exile; fugitive (7)
8 Gave way to pressure (7)
10 Material from which metal is extracted (3)
11 Grow feathers (6)
13 Entices (5)
14 Opposite one of two (5)
15 Superhero film based on comic characters (1-3)

No. 312
Tuesday November 8th 2022

Across

1 Antibiotic (10)
5 Celestial body (5)
7 Assembly (5)
9 Autographed something for a fan (6)
10 Type of house (abbrev) (4)
12 Type of music (4)
13 Frightens (6)
16 Eat steadily (5)
17 Carer (anag) (5)
18 Gathering of people (10)

Down

1 Written agreements (5)
2 Large towns (6)
3 Official records (4)
4 Having equality of measure (9)
6 Periodic publications (9)
8 23rd Greek letter (3)
11 Dung beetle (6)
12 Fruit preserve (3)
14 Woollen fabric (5)
15 Protective foot covering (4)

No. 313
Wednesday November 9th 2022

Across

3 Masticated (6)
6 Section of a long poem (5)
7 Small doors or gates (7)
9 Flour dough used in cooking (5)
12 Stealthy (11)
14 Pertaining to birth (5)
15 Game participants (7)
17 Unsuitable (5)
18 Creators (6)

Down

1 Tool that is useful for the Arctic (3,4)
2 Uncommon (7)
3 Lack of courage (9)
4 Frying pan (3)
5 Go out with (4)
8 Harmony (9)
10 Rise into the air (of an aircraft) (4,3)
11 Use up; exhaust (7)
13 Dejected (4)
16 Wild ox (3)

No. 314
Thursday November 10th 2022

Across

1 Complying with orders (8)
6 Compass point (5)
7 Pointed part of a fork (5)
9 Wish for (4)
10 Garment part that covers an arm (6)
12 ___ Currie: former politician (6)
14 Vertical spar on a ship (4)
17 Variety show (5)
18 Measures duration (5)
19 Defector (8)

Down

2 Element with atomic number 5 (5)
3 Sophie ___ : British model (4)
4 Forces out (6)
5 Ethos (anag) (5)
6 This starts on 1st January (3,4)
8 Segregated groups or areas (7)
11 Not noticed (6)
13 Vacillate (5)
15 Equipped (5)
16 Male deer (4)

No. 315
Friday November 11th 2022

Across

1 Ban for breaking a rule (10)
5 Lacking interest (5)
7 Derisive smile (5)
9 Hit hard (6)
10 Standard (4)
12 Ewers (4)
13 Brandy (6)
16 Fit with glass (5)
17 Regions (5)
18 Dry white wine (10)

Down

1 Female opera singers (5)
2 John ___ : US novelist (6)
3 Speech impediment (4)
4 Self-employed (9)
6 Distinct section of a piece of writing (9)
8 Fix the result in advance (3)
11 Trinidad and ___ : country (6)
12 Lively dance (3)
14 ___ Affleck: US actor (5)
15 Put on an item of clothing (4)

No. 316
Saturday November 12th 2022

Across

6 Having high status (11)
7 Ranked (5)
8 Third Greek letter (5)
9 Uma ___ : US actress (7)
12 Apportions a punishment (5)
13 Game of chance (5)
14 Hardware sellers (11)

Down

1 Lean or thin (5)
2 Poverty (11)
3 Sports grounds (8)
4 Societies (11)
5 ___ Hayes: US singer (5)
8 Betting (8)
10 Extent (5)
11 ___ Way: famous Roman road (5)

No. 317
Sunday November 13th 2022

Across
6 Rude (11)
7 Criminal deception (5)
9 Come to a point (5)
10 Separator (7)
13 Pools (anag) (5)
14 Country in the Arabian peninsula (5)
15 Goodwill (11)

Down
1 A moment (5)
2 Highs and lows (3,3,5)
3 Anniversary of when you are born (8)
4 Character; nature (11)
5 Harsh and serious in manner (5)
8 Tending to cause disagreement (8)
11 Bludgeons (5)
12 Leg joints (5)

No. 318
Monday November 14th 2022

Across
1 Receptacles (10)
5 Mournful song (5)
7 Type of bandage (5)
9 Hold in high esteem (6)
10 Plant used for flavouring (4)
12 Dean ___ : US actor who played Superman (4)
13 Learned person (6)
16 Evil spirit (5)
17 Hank of wool (5)
18 Exciting experiences (10)

Down
1 Programmer (5)
2 Wards off (6)
3 Facial feature (4)
4 Repeat (9)
6 Saved from punishment (9)
8 Mouth (informal) (3)
11 Breed of hound (6)
12 Scoundrel (3)
14 Military vehicles (5)
15 Sheet of floating ice (4)

No. 319
Tuesday November 15th 2022

Across

1 Colleagues (2-7)
5 Remove; excise (6)
7 Push; poke (4)
8 Stored away (7)
11 Has an impact on (7)
14 Mass of floating ice (4)
15 Exhaled audibly (6)
16 Avowed (9)

Down

1 Mark written under the letter c (7)
2 Wealthy (4-3)
3 Strong cords (5)
4 Arrive (4)
6 Large tracts of land (7)
9 Animal cages (7)
10 Definite; unquestionable (7)
12 Wingless jumping insect (4)
13 Keen (5)

No. 320
Wednesday November 16th 2022

Across

1 Lightweight garment (1-5)
4 Curved shape (4)
7 Smallest quantity (5)
8 Shrewdness; understanding (5)
9 Warhead carried by a missile (7)
11 Canopies (7)
13 Large spoon with a long handle (5)
14 Live by (5)
15 Plant stem part from which a leaf emerges (4)
16 Small hole (6)

Down

1 Spring flower (5)
2 Unnecessarily forceful (5-6)
3 Explanation (9)
5 Retail nerve (anag) (11)
6 Salma ___ : actress (5)
8 Sitting; seated (of a position) (9)
10 Criminal (5)
12 Perspire (5)

No. 321
Thursday November 17th 2022

Across

1 Astounds (10)
6 Distinctive atmosphere created by a person (4)
7 Ingenious device (6)
8 Assurance; composure (6)
9 Monetary unit of South Africa (4)
11 Lyric poems (4)
13 Exaggerate (6)
15 Best (6)
17 Modify (4)
18 Rate per hundred (10)

Down

2 Supplanted (7)
3 Shout of appreciation (5)
4 Lowest point (5)
5 That vessel (3)
7 Chatter (3)
10 Prodding with the elbow (7)
12 Remove wool from sheep (5)
13 Make a choice (3)
14 Happening (5)
16 Mischievous sprite (3)

No. 322
Friday November 18th 2022

Across

2 Cornmeal (7)
5 Capital of Vietnam (5)
6 Cautious (7)
7 Make a map of (5)
10 Gadget (11)
12 Firearm (5)
13 Eyelash cosmetic (7)
14 Stagger (5)
15 Takes small bites (7)

Down

1 Mysterious (7)
2 Painting; photograph (7)
3 Saw; observed (4)
4 Association created for mutual benefit (8)
7 Plant of the primrose family (8)
8 Winding shapes (7)
9 Varies (7)
11 Protective crust (4)

No. 323
Saturday November 19th 2022

Across

- **6** Introductory (11)
- **7** Crave; desire (5)
- **8** Piece of land (5)
- **9** Small songbird; singer (7)
- **12** People not ordained (5)
- **13** Germaine ___ : Australian author (5)
- **14** Pyotr ___ : Russian composer (11)

Down

- **1** Aromatic flavouring (5)
- **2** Serious or influential (11)
- **3** Recently (8)
- **4** Ghost (11)
- **5** Legendary stories (5)
- **8** Knowing many languages (8)
- **10** Coin entry points in machines (5)
- **11** Dull colours (5)

No. 324
Sunday November 20th 2022

Across

- **3** Breathless (6)
- **6** Be the same as (5)
- **7** Sour in taste (7)
- **9** Musical speeds (5)
- **12** Highest class in society (11)
- **14** Correct (5)
- **15** Confused struggle (7)
- **17** Ire (5)
- **18** Gas we breathe (6)

Down

- **1** In the middle (7)
- **2** Tumult (7)
- **3** Person bringing a legal case (9)
- **4** Coniferous tree (3)
- **5** Platform (4)
- **8** Having luxurious tastes (9)
- **10** Luggage (7)
- **11** Puzzle (7)
- **13** Sound reflection (4)
- **16** Cook in hot oil (3)

No. 325
Monday November 21st 2022

Across
1 Little known (9)
5 Makes fun of someone (6)
7 Total spread of a bridge (4)
8 Be made of (7)
11 Excited agreeably (7)
14 Effervesce (4)
15 Harsh (6)
16 Succinctly (9)

Down
1 Go back on (7)
2 Traditional example (7)
3 Long pointed teeth (5)
4 Ventilates; supporters (4)
6 Light periods of rainfall (7)
9 Examine (7)
10 Ornamental stone openwork (7)
12 Large wading bird (4)
13 Musical toy (5)

No. 326
Tuesday November 22nd 2022

Across
1 Impersonations (11)
8 Join together (5)
9 Expressive (of music) (7)
10 Neutral (11)
13 Injurious (7)
14 Lift up (5)
15 Distribute again (11)

Down
2 Financier (6)
3 Art of carving (9)
4 Roman poet (4)
5 Apparently (9)
6 Incompetent person (9)
7 Pile of refuse (9)
11 Sightseeing trip in Africa (6)
12 Document allowing entry to a country (4)

No. 327
Wednesday November 23rd 2022

Across

2 Occurring in the absence of oxygen (9)
7 Female chicken (3)
8 Deceit; trickery (9)
9 Vindicate (9)
10 China (9)
11 Piece of land for cultivation (9)
13 Pub (3)
14 Eg an accent or cedilla (9)

Down

1 State of the USA (5,6)
2 Additionally (3)
3 Car pedal (11)
4 Substitute (11)
5 Newly-wed (5)
6 Astonishing (11)
10 Lively Bohemian dance (5)
12 Twitch (3)

No. 328
Thursday November 24th 2022

Across

6 Trifling sum of money (5,6)
7 Be alive; be real (5)
9 Impertinent; cheeky (5)
10 Eyelet placed in a hole (7)
13 Components (5)
14 Foolishly credulous (5)
15 Dismantle (11)

Down

1 Awry (5)
2 A redeeming quality (6,5)
3 Eg rooks and knights (8)
4 Diligent (11)
5 Precious stone (5)
8 Handouts (anag) (8)
11 Tool used for digging (5)
12 Triangular river mouth (5)

No. 329
Friday November 25th 2022

Across

6 Movement towards a destination (11)
7 Rejuvenate (5)
8 Escapade (5)
9 Lead batsmen (cricket) (7)
12 Liquid measure (5)
13 ___ John: Rocket Man singer (5)
14 Type of weather system (11)

Down

1 Gush out in a jet (5)
2 Sensible and practical (4,2,5)
3 Intimidate (8)
4 Mood (11)
5 Knotty protuberance on a tree (5)
8 Lenience (8)
10 Crouch (5)
11 Arm of a body of water (5)

No. 330
Saturday November 26th 2022

Across

1 Tremor following an earthquake (10)
5 Saying (5)
7 Neck warmer (5)
9 Jumped on one leg (6)
10 Fluent but shallow (4)
12 Seventh month of the year (4)
13 Medical treatment place (6)
16 Dirt (5)
17 Thick woollen fabric (5)
18 Likely to attack; belligerent (10)

Down

1 Embarrass (5)
2 Had a very strong smell (6)
3 Part of a door fastening (4)
4 Demanding situation (9)
6 Horrifying (9)
8 Lie (3)
11 Flat dishes (6)
12 Sharp projection (3)
14 Get by begging (5)
15 Rage (anag) (4)

No. 331
Sunday November 27th 2022

Across
1 Elapsed (of time) (6)
4 Mire (anag) (4)
7 Tugs (5)
8 Dividing boundaries (5)
9 Freedom to deviate from fact (7)
11 Disparaging remarks (7)
13 ___ Streep: actress (5)
14 Unit of weight (5)
15 Clean up (4)
16 Lower someone's dignity (6)

Down
1 Proceeding from the pope (5)
2 Egotistical (4-7)
3 Indispensable (9)
5 Hostility (11)
6 Dry biscuits used as baby food (5)
8 Rock used for sharpening tools (9)
10 The entire scale (5)
12 Shininess (5)

No. 332
Monday November 28th 2022

Across
2 Worked out logically (7)
6 Tray (anag) (4)
9 Item for catching fish (3)
10 Food pantries (7)
11 Act of staying away from work (11)
12 Belief (7)
13 Tear (3)
14 What you walk on (4)
15 Fifth Greek letter (7)

Down
1 Comradeship (11)
3 Recklessly impetuous person (9)
4 Sense of right and wrong (10)
5 Having definite limits (11)
7 Items used by astronomers (10)
8 First in order of importance (9)

No. 333
Tuesday November 29th 2022

Across

1 Great Bear (constellation) (4,5)
6 Creep (5)
7 Words that identify things (5)
9 Snarled (anag) (7)
12 Pursues (7)
16 Composition for a solo instrument (5)
17 Concealing garments (5)
18 Thoroughly soaked (9)

Down

2 This covers your body (4)
3 Creates (5)
4 Small group ruling a country (5)
5 Competition stages (6)
6 Light spongy baked dish (7)
8 Large dark low cloud (7)
10 Legal rule (3)
11 Collections of photos (6)
13 Not concealed (5)
14 Divide by cutting (5)
15 Present (4)

No. 334
Wednesday November 30th 2022

Across

2 Stammered (9)
7 Flightless bird (3)
8 Iniquitous (9)
9 Compels by coercion (9)
10 Home (9)
11 Impersonation (9)
13 Monstrous humanoid creature (3)
14 Person who delivers news (9)

Down

1 Philosophical doctrine (11)
2 What our planet orbits (3)
3 Unlucky (11)
4 Menacing (11)
5 Chambers (5)
6 Dejection (11)
10 These grow on your head (5)
12 Boolean operator (3)

No. 335
Thursday December 1st 2022

Across

1 Depressions (4)
3 Showing gentleness (6)
7 Round cap (5)
9 Killer whales (5)
10 Starting points (7)
11 Harden (7)
13 Burning (5)
14 Ignite (5)
15 Not disposed to cheat (6)
16 Medium-sized feline (4)

Down

1 Remove errors from software (5)
2 Persistent harassment (11)
4 Affecting the feelings (9)
5 Misleadingly (11)
6 Ascends (5)
8 Lacking force (9)
11 Instruct (5)
12 Milky fluid found in some plants (5)

No. 336
Friday December 2nd 2022

Across

2 More straightforward (7)
6 Tidy (4)
9 Beer container (3)
10 Molasses (7)
11 Person with strong patriotic feelings (11)
12 Observed (7)
13 Support for a golf ball (3)
14 Image of a god (4)
15 Decorative patterns (7)

Down

1 Not joined together (11)
3 Bad luck (9)
4 Of similar opinion (4-6)
5 Unfortunate (11)
7 Shrewdness (10)
8 Sickening (9)

No. 337
Saturday December 3rd 2022

Across

2 Actings (anag) (7)
5 Wild dog of Australia (5)
6 Newsworthy (7)
7 Divided into two (5)
10 Eg Queen of Hearts (7,4)
12 Timber framework (5)
13 Spiral cavity of the inner ear (7)
14 Large woody plants (5)
15 Childbirth assistant (7)

Down

1 Patella (7)
2 Have within (7)
3 Type of wood (4)
4 Explosive shells (8)
7 Pepper plant (8)
8 Disturb (7)
9 Becomes fully grown (7)
11 Sailing vessel (4)

No. 338
Sunday December 4th 2022

Across

1 Metric unit of length (10)
5 Hushed (5)
7 Personnel at work (5)
9 Complex carbohydrate (6)
10 Not stereo (4)
12 Song for a solo voice (4)
13 Adoring (6)
16 Cutting instrument (5)
17 Commence (5)
18 Intolerable (10)

Down

1 Arrives (5)
2 Charge with a crime (6)
3 The Orient (4)
4 Process of forming logical conclusions (9)
6 Custom (9)
8 ___ Rida: American rapper (3)
11 Thief (6)
12 Put a question to (3)
14 Spirit in a bottle (5)
15 Venerable ___ : English monk (4)

No. 339
Monday December 5th 2022

Across
1 Mock (6)
4 Told an untruth (4)
7 Speaks (5)
8 Badgers' homes (5)
9 Unit of square measure (7)
11 Hates (7)
13 Stylish (5)
14 Put in considerable effort (5)
15 ___ and wherefores: reasons for something (4)
16 Fire-breathing monster (6)

Down
1 Pertaining to the Netherlands (5)
2 Unwillingly (11)
3 Cowardly and despicable (9)
5 Absorbing; intriguing (11)
6 Cleans (5)
8 Observer (9)
10 Tough fibrous tissue (5)
12 Country in NE Africa (5)

No. 340
Tuesday December 6th 2022

Across
2 Fatigue (9)
7 Tree (3)
8 Child (9)
9 Unhurried (9)
10 Scheme (9)
11 Fluent use of language (9)
13 Sheltered side (3)
14 Dissipation (9)

Down
1 Place where fighting occurs (11)
2 For what purpose (3)
3 Type of treatment using needles (11)
4 Component parts (11)
5 Act of going in (5)
6 Witches (11)
10 Natural satellites (5)
12 Former measure of length (3)

No. 341
Wednesday December 7th 2022

Across

1 ___ artichoke: vegetable (9)
6 Island in the Bay of Naples (5)
7 Invigorating medicine (5)
9 ___ seat: aircraft safety device (7)
12 Type of xylophone (7)
16 Not tense (5)
17 Form of humour (5)
18 Straitens (anag) (9)

Down

2 Ready to eat (4)
3 Chute (5)
4 Machine for shaping wood or metal (5)
5 Sixty seconds (6)
6 Sugar heated until it turns brown (7)
8 Restaurant serving roast meats (7)
10 Position of employment (3)
11 Passion (6)
13 Encounters (5)
14 Zodiac sign (5)
15 Garment of ancient Rome (4)

No. 342
Thursday December 8th 2022

Across

1 Artful person (6)
4 Complacent (4)
7 Full of life (5)
8 Monetary unit of Serbia (5)
9 Becomes less wide (7)
11 Public speakers (7)
13 Pool of money (5)
14 ___ Woodward: rugby union coach (5)
15 Free from doubt (4)
16 Sayings (6)

Down

1 Twelve (5)
2 Agent who supplies goods to stores (11)
3 The origin of a word (9)
5 Hard to imagine; astonishing (4-7)
6 Spiny yellow plant (5)
8 Held at arms length (9)
10 Fists (5)
12 Paces (5)

No. 343
Friday December 9th 2022

Across

1 System of government (11)
7 This evening (7)
8 Once more (5)
9 About (5)
11 Detection technology (5)
12 Looks after (5)
13 Average (7)
16 Contriving to bring about (11)

Down

1 Wager (3)
2 Flee (3)
3 Where one finds Kabul (11)
4 Calamity or great loss (11)
5 Introduced air to (7)
6 Less old (7)
9 Customs of a society (7)
10 Precipitating (7)
14 22nd Greek letter (3)
15 Limb used for walking (3)

No. 344
Saturday December 10th 2022

Across

1 Worthy of reward (9)
5 Manly (6)
7 Flightless birds (4)
8 Tall tower (7)
11 Temporary measure (7)
14 Undergarment (4)
15 Deep serving dish (6)
16 Percussion instrument (9)

Down

1 Sly (7)
2 Hot wind blowing from North Africa (7)
3 Female relation (5)
4 Bend or coil (4)
6 Take out (7)
9 Inactive pill (7)
10 Enunciate (7)
12 Arduous journey (4)
13 Concise and full of meaning (5)

No. 345
Sunday December 11th 2022

Across

1 Magnifying instrument (10)
5 Type of coffee (5)
7 Capital of South Korea (5)
9 Abilities; talents (6)
10 Opening for air; outlet (4)
12 Ox-like mammals (4)
13 Time that is to come (6)
16 Moderate and well-balanced (5)
17 Submerged ridges of rock (5)
18 Contemptibly (10)

Down

1 Beasts of burden (5)
2 Frankly (6)
3 Price (4)
4 Way of doing something (9)
6 Conceivable (9)
8 Auction item (3)
11 Heading on a document (6)
12 Absolutely (3)
14 Piece of writing (5)
15 Fall; prod (anag) (4)

No. 346
Monday December 12th 2022

Across

6 Very busy and full (5-1-5)
7 Planet (5)
9 Type of stopwatch (5)
10 Sculptures (7)
13 Samantha ___ : Irish singer (5)
14 Hurled away (5)
15 Assuredly (11)

Down

1 Unpleasant facial expression (5)
2 Sustenance (11)
3 Block (8)
4 Express sympathy (11)
5 Avoid; garment (5)
8 Theatrical (8)
11 Hit hard (5)
12 Moves in the wind (5)

No. 347
Tuesday December 13th 2022

Across

6 Retained part of a cheque (11)
7 Research deeply (5)
8 Recipient of money (5)
9 Musical ending (7)
12 Keep away from (5)
13 Set of moral principles (5)
14 Callous (11)

Down

1 Rushes along; skims (5)
2 Inn (6,5)
3 Went along to an event (8)
4 Institute of higher education (11)
5 Moves through the air (5)
8 Worldwide outbreak (8)
10 ___ Major: constellation (5)
11 Pains (5)

No. 348
Wednesday December 14th 2022

Across

6 Legacy (11)
7 Onwards in time (5)
9 Feelings and emotions (5)
10 Hawker (7)
13 Shelf (5)
14 Heroic tales (5)
15 Break off; stop (11)

Down

1 Fifes (anag) (5)
2 Specialist in care for the feet (11)
3 Impetus (8)
4 Urging on (11)
5 Recycle (5)
8 Fence formed by bushes (8)
11 Lumps of earth (5)
12 Put a question to (5)

No. 349
Thursday December 15th 2022

Across
1 Built (11)
7 Made bare (7)
8 Crumble (5)
9 Egg-shaped (5)
11 Hazardous; dangerous (5)
12 Gleam; glitter (5)
13 Part of a fortification (7)
16 Elucidated by using an example (11)

Down
1 Signal for action (3)
2 Bite sharply (3)
3 Huge three-horned dinosaur (11)
4 Financial sponsor (11)
5 Crowds of people (7)
6 Propriety (7)
9 Art of paper-folding (7)
10 Act of turning up (7)
14 Cereal grain (3)
15 Child (3)

No. 350
Friday December 16th 2022

Across
1 Eg Anna or minim (10)
5 Type of small fastener (5)
7 ___ of Lebanon: tree (5)
9 Token (6)
10 Petty quarrel (4)
12 Sixth month of the year (4)
13 Loud disturbance (6)
16 ___ Fury: British boxer (5)
17 Language of the Romans (5)
18 Delicious (of food) (10)

Down
1 Annoying insects (5)
2 Isaac ___ : physicist (6)
3 Loose scrum (rugby) (4)
4 Fielding position in cricket (3-6)
6 Recall past experiences (9)
8 Umpire (abbrev) (3)
11 Hammerlike tool (6)
12 Note down (3)
14 Colour lightly (5)
15 ___ Hathaway: actress (4)

No. 351
Saturday December 17th 2022

Across

1 All-round view (8)
6 Tiny part of an image (5)
7 Sweet flavoured drink (5)
9 Writing instruments (4)
10 Danish monetary unit (pl) (6)
12 Itemised (6)
14 ___ Pound: US poet (4)
17 Settle for sleep (of birds) (5)
18 Monastery superior (5)
19 Prompt (8)

Down

2 Plant hormone (5)
3 Solely (4)
4 Renounce an oath (6)
5 The lion who rules over Narnia (5)
6 Liked by many people (7)
8 Rich dessert (7)
11 Church official (6)
13 Tread heavily (5)
15 Striped animal (5)
16 Deliberately taunt (4)

No. 352
Sunday December 18th 2022

Across

2 Wine merchant (7)
5 Measuring instrument (5)
6 Fail to care for (7)
7 Let air escape from a valve (5)
10 Sponsor mice (anag) (11)
12 Tool for boring holes (5)
13 Rational; reasonable (7)
14 Gives temporarily (5)
15 Acutely (7)

Down

1 Repositories of antiques (7)
2 Sellers (7)
3 Story (4)
4 Fee paid to use someone's services when required (8)
7 Rod-shaped bacterium (8)
8 Normally (7)
9 Sounding a bell (7)
11 Rank (4)

No. 353
Monday December 19th 2022

Across

1 Johannes ___ : German composer (6)
4 Exploits (4)
7 Violent weather (5)
8 Send someone to a medical specialist (5)
9 Schematic (7)
11 Sheriff's officer (7)
13 Cavalry sword (5)
14 Benefactor (5)
15 Every (4)
16 Made a victim of (6)

Down

1 Beads (anag) (5)
2 Fearful of open spaces (11)
3 Easily remembered (9)
5 Adequacy (11)
6 ___ Harding: Girls Aloud singer (5)
8 Quantity that is left over (9)
10 Out of fashion (5)
12 Unit of capacitance (5)

No. 354
Tuesday December 20th 2022

Across

1 Carpenter (10)
5 Loathe (5)
7 The reproduction of sound (5)
9 Inner part of a seed (6)
10 Allot a punishment (4)
12 Hilltop (4)
13 Dry and brittle (of food) (6)
16 Less moist (5)
17 Entrance hallway (5)
18 Fast food items (10)

Down

1 Strike very hard (5)
2 Network of rabbit burrows (6)
3 Thoroughfare (4)
4 Infinitely (9)
6 Mouth organ (9)
8 Lyric poem (3)
11 Like better (6)
12 Auction offer (3)
14 Linear measures of three feet (5)
15 Child's bed (4)

No. 355
Wednesday December 21st 2022

Across

1 Small pet rodent (6)
4 Russian monarch (4)
7 Sailing vessel (5)
8 Lindsay ___ : actress (5)
9 Listening (7)
11 Toxin in the body (7)
13 Lying flat (5)
14 Made a mistake (5)
15 Yellow part of an egg (4)
16 Spiny-finned fish (6)

Down

1 Sculptured symbol (5)
2 Type of music (4,3,4)
3 Complicated (9)
5 Female students (11)
6 Tarns (anag) (5)
8 Unit of astronomical distance (5,4)
10 Be relevant (5)
12 Prod with one's elbow (5)

No. 356
Thursday December 22nd 2022

Across

1 Sprite of Irish folklore (10)
5 Prison compartments (5)
7 Strength (5)
9 Crouches down (6)
10 Primitive plant (4)
12 Strand; lock (4)
13 Reactive metal (6)
16 Fatigued (5)
17 Big cat (5)
18 Tumbledown (10)

Down

1 Scottish lakes (5)
2 Not real or genuine (6)
3 Publicise in an exaggerated manner (4)
4 Reluctant (9)
6 US state (9)
8 Chris ___ : English singer (3)
11 ___ mundum: defying everyone (6)
12 Exclamation of amazement (3)
14 ___ Simpson: cartoon character (5)
15 Hair colourants (4)

No. 357
Friday December 23rd 2022

Across

3 Less warm (6)
6 Common edible fruit (5)
7 Living in another's home (7)
9 Ironic metaphor (5)
12 Attentive; ultra-careful (11)
14 Core group; basic unit (5)
15 Two lines of verse (7)
17 Cairo is in this country (5)
18 Recompense for hardship (6)

Down

1 Portable computers (7)
2 Assign (7)
3 Heavenly (9)
4 Excavated soil (3)
5 Speak in a wild way (4)
8 Turned off course (9)
10 These follow Sundays (7)
11 Characteristics (7)
13 Number after three (4)
16 Animal foot (3)

No. 358
Saturday December 24th 2022

Across

2 Shock physically (5-2)
6 Relax and do little (4)
9 Interdict (3)
10 Bodies of writing (7)
11 Crushed with sorrow (11)
12 Intrinsic nature (7)
13 Joke (3)
14 Test (anag) (4)
15 Admire deeply (7)

Down

1 Plant-eating insect (11)
3 Loathsome (9)
4 Wall of earth for holding back water (10)
5 Celebrity (11)
7 Eg baptism and matrimony (10)
8 Bizarre; shocking (9)

No. 359
Sunday December 25th 2022

Across

2 Official identification documents (9)
7 21st Greek letter (3)
8 Venetian boatman (9)
9 Out of bounds (3-6)
10 Politician (9)
11 Bring about (9)
13 One's family (3)
14 Customers collectively (9)

Down

1 Substance that arouses desire (11)
2 Hog (3)
3 Act of publishing in several places (11)
4 Multiply (11)
5 Precipitates (5)
6 Encircling (11)
10 Japanese dish (5)
12 Eek (anag) (3)

No. 360
Monday December 26th 2022

Across

3 Heart (slang) (6)
6 Stand up (5)
7 Insanity (7)
9 Brace (5)
12 Comprehends (11)
14 Happen (5)
15 Smooth and soft (7)
17 Ahead of time (5)
18 Tangled (of hair) (6)

Down

1 Holy place (7)
2 Four-legged reptiles (7)
3 Moderate (9)
4 Range of knowledge (3)
5 Expose to danger (4)
8 Ruined (9)
10 Single-horned creature (7)
11 Fish-eating birds of prey (7)
13 Smile broadly (4)
16 Animal doctor (3)

No. 361
Tuesday December 27th 2022

Across

2 Very great (3-4)
5 Pertaining to sound (5)
6 Last longer than (7)
7 Lumberjack (5)
10 Allowed (11)
12 General hatred (5)
13 Scowls (7)
14 Perfect (5)
15 Children's carers (7)

Down

1 Ignorant of something (7)
2 Eighth sign of the zodiac (7)
3 Bird of prey (4)
4 Tree of the birch family (8)
7 Seven-sided polygon (8)
8 Diffusion of molecules through a membrane (7)
9 Duty-bound (7)
11 Link a town with another (4)

No. 362
Wednesday December 28th 2022

Across

2 Rescued (anag) (7)
6 Throb (4)
9 Drink a little (3)
10 Make bigger (7)
11 Prophetic of the end of the world (11)
12 Discharge from a hole in a pipe (7)
13 Lad (3)
14 Amaze (4)
15 Sticks to (7)

Down

1 Country in South West Asia (5,6)
3 Church minister (9)
4 Pique (10)
5 Expressing disapproval of (11)
7 Secret symbol (10)
8 University one attended (4,5)

No. 363
Thursday December 29th 2022

Across

2 Silvery-white metal (7)
5 Path or road (5)
6 Vocabulary list (7)
7 Slips (anag) (5)
10 Eg share news (11)
12 Solids with six equal square faces (5)
13 Building (7)
14 Garden buildings (5)
15 Most important (7)

Down

1 Copious (7)
2 Temperature scale (7)
3 Central (4)
4 Fictional ugly creatures (8)
7 Famous Scottish lake (4,4)
8 Bishop's jurisdiction (7)
9 Walks for pleasure (7)
11 At a distance (4)

No. 364
Friday December 30th 2022

Across

1 Astonish (9)
6 Friend (Spanish) (5)
7 Circumference (5)
9 Lack of (7)
12 Coincide partially (7)
16 Unit of light (5)
17 Question intensely (5)
18 Shocked (9)

Down

2 Letters and parcels generally (4)
3 Plants of a region (5)
4 Strong desires (5)
5 Boldness (6)
6 Newtlike salamander (7)
8 Attentive (7)
10 Tropical constrictor (3)
11 Assumed propositions (6)
13 Of the moon (5)
14 Grape (anag) (5)
15 Sound of a snake (4)

No. 365
Saturday December 31st 2022

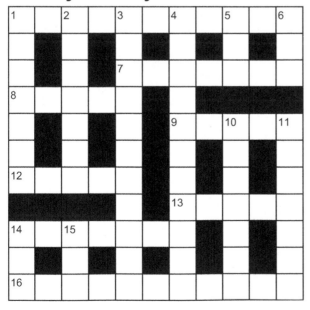

Across
6 Forged (11)
7 Discharged a weapon (5)
9 Male bee (5)
10 Voter (7)
13 Starting point (5)
14 Push away (5)
15 Dividing line (11)

Down
1 Eat quickly (5)
2 Argumentative (11)
3 Person owed money (8)
4 Sector of a population (11)
5 Warhorse (5)
8 Kitchen sideboards (8)
11 Home (5)
12 Side of a large object (5)

No. 366
Sunday January 1st 2023

Across
1 Uninvited guest (11)
7 Eight-sided polygon (7)
8 A finger or toe (5)
9 Ashley ___ : actress (5)
12 Strong currents of air (5)
13 Damp (5)
14 Express great joy (7)
16 Arousing pleasure but also pain (11)

Down
1 Making an unpowered flight (7)
2 Particular languages (7)
3 Where washing is hung to dry (7,4)
4 Stargazers (11)
5 Embrace (3)
6 ___ Weasley: friend of Harry Potter (3)
10 Satisfy (7)
11 Most tidy (7)
14 Cause friction (3)
15 Stream of liquid (3)

Solutions

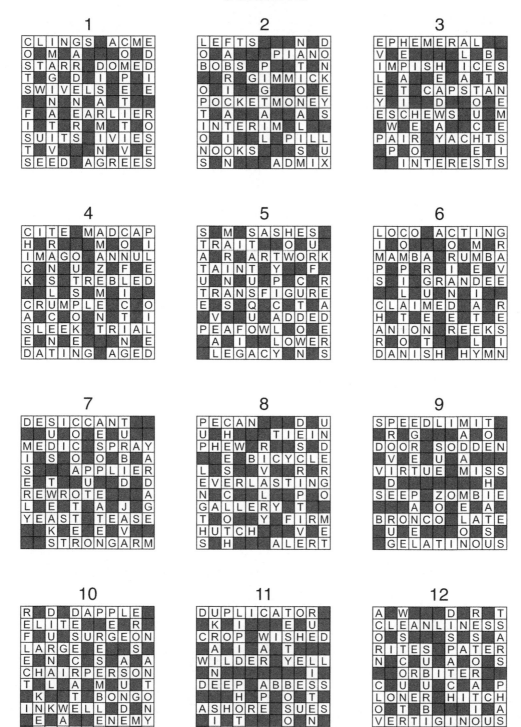

Solutions

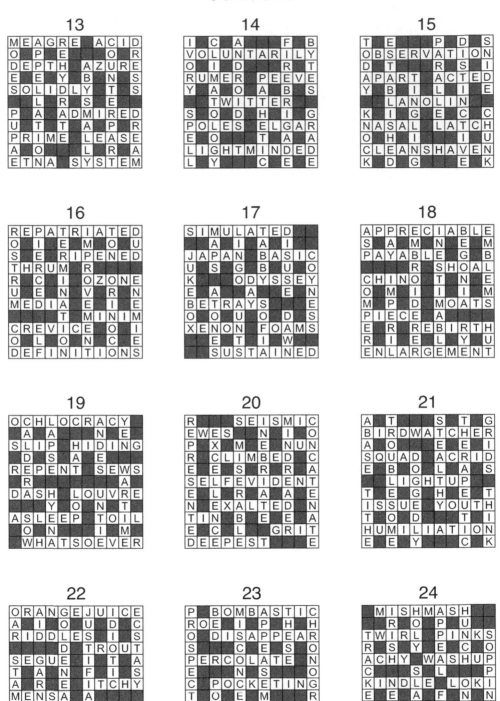

13

M	E	A	G	R	E		A	C	I	D
O		P		E			O		R	
D	E	P	T	H		A	Z	U	R	E
E		E		Y		B		N		S
S	O	L	I	D	L	Y		T		S
		L		R		S	E			
P	A		A	D	M	I	R	E	D	
U		T		T		A		P		R
P	R	I	M	E		L	E	A	S	E
A		O				L		R		A
E	T	N	A		S	Y	S	T	E	M

14

I		C		A			F		B	
V	O	L	U	N	T	A	R	I	L	Y
O		I		D			R		T	
R	U	M	E	R		P	E	E	V	E
Y		A		O		A	B		S	
		T	W	I	T	T	E	R		
S	O		D		H		I		G	
P	O	L	E	S		E	L	G	A	R
E		O				T		A	A	
L	I	G	H	T	M	I	N	D	E	D
L		Y			C		E		E	

15

T		E		P		D		S		
O	B	S	E	R	V	A	T	I	O	N
D		T		R		S		I		
A	P	A	R	T		A	C	T	E	D
Y		B		I		L		I		E
	L	A	N	O	L	I	N			
K		I		G		E		C		C
N	A	S	A	L		L	A	T	C	H
O		H		I			I		I	U
C	L	E	A	N	S	H	A	V	E	N
K		D		G			E		E	K

16

R	E	P	A	T	R	I	A	T	E	D
O		I		E		M		O		U
S		E	R	I	P	E	N	E	D	
T	H	R	U	M		R		O		O
R		C		I		O	Z	O	N	E
U		E		N		V		R		N
M	E	D	I	A		E		I		E
		T		M	I	N	I	M		
C	R	E	V	I	C	E		O		I
O		L		O		C		N		E
D	E	F	I	N	I	T	I	O	N	S

17

S	I	M	U	L	A	T	E	D		
	A		I		A		I			
J	A	P	A	N		B	A	S	I	C
U		S		G		B		U		O
K		O	D	Y	S	S	E	Y		
E		A		A		E		N		
B	E	T	R	A	Y	S		E		E
O		O		U		O	D	S		
X	E	N	O	N		F	O	A	M	S
		E		T		I		W		
S	U	S	T	A	I	N	E	D		

18

A	P	P	R	E	C	I	A	B	L	E
S		A		M		N		E		M
P	A	Y	A	B	L	E		G		B
		R			R		S	H	O	A	L
C	H	I	N	O		T		N		E
O		M		I		I		I		M
M	P		D		M	O	A	T	S	
P	I	E	C	E		A				
E		R		R	E	B	I	R	T	H
R		I		E		L		Y		U
E	N	L	A	R	G	E	M	E	N	T

19

O	C	H	L	O	C	R	A	C	Y	
	A		A		N		E			
S	L	I	P		H	I	D	I	N	G
	D		S		A		E			
R	E	P	E	N	T		S	E	W	S
	R								A	
D	A	S	H		L	O	U	V	R	E
	Y		O		N		T			
A	S	L	E	E	P		T	O	I	L
	O		N				I		M	
W	H	A	T	S	O	E	V	E	R	

20

R			S	E	I	S	M	I	C	
E	W	E	S		N		I		O	
P		X		M	E		N	U	N	
R		C	L	I	M	B	E	D		C
E		E		S		R		R		A
S	E	L	F	E	V	I	D	E	N	T
E		L		R		A		A		E
N		E	X	A	L	T	E	D		N
T	I	N		B		E		E		A
E		C		L			G	R	I	T
D	E	E	P	E	S	T				E

21

A		T			S		T		G	
B	I	R	D	W	A	T	C	H	E	R
A		O			E		E		I	
S	Q	U	A	D		A	C	R	I	D
E		B		O		L			S	
		L	I	G	H	T	U	P		
T		E		G		H		E		T
I	S	S	U	E		Y	O	U	T	H
T		O		D			T		I	
H	U	M	I	L	I	A	T	I	O	N
E		E		Y			C		K	

22

O	R	A	N	G	E	J	U	I	C	E
A		I		O		U		D		C
R	I	D	D	L	E	S		I		S
		D			T	R	O	U	T	
S	E	G	U	E		I		T		A
T		A		N		F		I		S
A	R	E	I	T	C	H	Y			S
M	E	N	S	A		A				
I		I		G	I	B	B	O	N	S
N		S		L		L		W		I
A	C	H	I	E	V	E	M	E	N	T

23

P		B	O	M	B	A	S	T	I	C
R	O	E		I		P		H		H
O		D	I	S	A	P	P	E	A	R
S		C		E		S		O		O
P	E	R	C	O	L	A	T	E		N
E			N		S		S			O
C		P	O	C	K	E	T	I	N	G
T		O		E		M			R	
I	N	S	P	I	T	E	O	F		A
V		E		V		N		L	I	P
E	A	R	N	E	S	T	L	Y		H

24

M	I	S	H	M	A	S	H			
		R		O		P	U			
T	W	I	R	L		P	I	N	K	S
R		S		Y		E		C		O
A	C	H	Y		W	A	S	H	U	P
C			S		L			P		P
K	I	N	D	L	E		L	O	K	I
E		E		A		F		N		N
R	E	V	E	L		U	S	I	N	G
		E		O		L		O		
		R	U	M	B	L	I	N	G	

Solutions

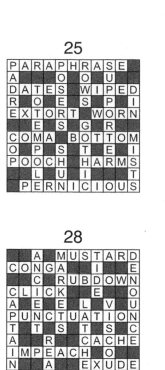

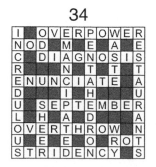

25

```
P A R A P H R A S E
A   O   O   U
D A T E S   W I P E D
R   O   E   S   P   I
E X T O R T   W O R N
  E   S   G   R
C O M A   B O T T O M
O   P   S   T   E   I
P O O C H   H A R M S
  L   U   I   T
P E R N I C I O U S
```

26

```
  A   B A T H T U B
M A N N A   O     E
  Y   R E Q U E S T
U M B E R   R     R
N   O   A   C   A   A
A U D A C I O U S L Y
W   Y   K   M   S   E
A   L   P R I E D
R O T U N D A   G
E   R   R A N K S
S Q U E E Z E   S
```

27

```
G   F   A V O W A L
A L O O F   A     I
M   X   F L E X I N G
B E T E L   S   K
L   R   U   S   F   I
E X O N E R A T I O N
D   T   N   Y   N   V
  C   C   I R A T E
P L O V E R S   L   R
  E   A   T O L L S
F E N C E S   Y   E
```

28

```
  A   M U S T A R D
C O N G A   I     E
  C   R U B D O W N
C L I C K   E     O
A   E   E   L   V   U
P U N C T U A T I O N
T   T   S   T   S   C
A   R   C A C H E
I M P E A C H   O
N   A   E X U D E
S P I D E R S   S
```

29

```
S C A R C E L Y
  Y   O   M   E
R A C E S   B U L L S
E   L   Y   E   L   U
P E E R   C R U S T S
E   E   E   S     P
A U T U M N   A C N E
L   H   B   O   O   N
S H A L L   V I V I D
  W   E   E   E
  S E M I N A R Y
```

30

```
C R A N K S H A F T
U     I   A   A
S P A S M   C I L I A
H   B   O   K   S   A
Y E A R N S   F I S H
  N   O   C   F
B O D Y   T H E I R S
E   O   J   I   E   Y
G E N R E   L A D E N
  E   A   L     O
I D E N T I F I E D
```

31

```
A   C   V   M   U
G H O S T L I N E S S
A   N   O   G   U
P A V E D   L L A M A
E   E   E   A   L
  R I S O T T O
A   T   C   E   P   S
P R I O R   S T O R K
A   B   I   L   I
C A L I B R A T I O N
E   E   E     S   S
```

32

```
W E P T   A D J U S T
R   O   O   I   N   E
E A R N S   S E R V E
A   T   U   C   E   T
K   R   P H A R A O H
  A   E   R   S
S T I R R E D   O   C
I   T   S   E   N   O
D R I F T   D A I L Y
L   S   A     N   L
E A T E R S   U G L Y
```

33

```
T R I P L E J U M P
I     A   A   O
R U L E S   P L U M B
E   I   T   E   S   A
S I M P E R   H E L P
  I   D   S   T
M O T E   M E T R I C
A   L   K   X   A   H
P A E A N   T E P E E
  S   E   E     S
E S S E N T I A L S
```

34

```
I   O V E R P O W E R
N O D   M   E   A   E
C   D I A G N O S I S
R   N   T   T   T
E N U N C I A T E   A
D   I   H     U
U   S E P T E M B E R
L   H   A   D     A
O V E R T H R O W N
U   E   E   O   R O T
S T R I D E N C Y   S
```

35

```
C   I   C H A R M S
L A R G O   O     E
E   K   N O O D L E S
R E S E T   I   R
I   O   R   N   H   A
C O M P A R T M E N T
S   E   L   M   A   T
  L   T   E E R I E
C O N J O I N   S   S
  O   A   T O A S T
P O W E R S   Y   S
```

36

```
O     P O L A R I S
C O R N   I   E   E
C   E   O   G   C U R
U   L I N E A G E   E
R   U   S   M   P   N
R E C O L L E C T E D
E   T   A   N   A   I
N   A Q U A T I C   P
C O N   G   S   L   I
E   H   B E E T
S W E E T E N   Y
```

Solutions

37

38

39

40

41

42

43

44

45

46

47

48

Solutions

49

```
A R T I F I C E R . U
U O . L . E . E O N
D O T M A T R I X . W
I . A . B . T . . I
O . L U B R I C A N T
V . E . . F . . T
I M M E R S I O N . I N
S . . G . C . T . N
U . D I A N A R I G G
A N Y . S . T . N . L
L . E X T R E M I T Y
```

50

```
C R A V A T . S C U D
O . C . P . . O . E
S T R I P . S A U D I
T . I . E . U . N . T
A M M E T E R . T . Y
. O . I . P . E
G . N . S P R I N G S
I . I . E . I . A . E
F L O U R . S I N C E
T . U . E . C . D
S A S H . E S T E R S
```

51

```
M . . U N T R U T H
I R A N . E . N . I
C . P . C . L . F E D
R . P I O N E E R . E
O . A . G . S . I . A
S P R I N G C L E A N
C . E . I . O . N . D
O . N O T E P A D . S
P I T . I . E . L . E
E . L . O . . T Y P E
S A Y I N G S . . K
```

52

```
N O N C H A L A N T
I . . . E . O . I
C H I N A . U R G E D
E . N . R . D . H . U
R O T A T E . S T U B
. E . S . N . C
F O R M . B U I L D S
O . A . E . C . U . O
X Y L E M . L I B E L
. I . M . E . . A
. B A B Y S I T T E R
```

53

```
S C H E M E . S W A M
I . I . I . . I . U
D O S E S . A L T O S
E . T . H . N . C . E
D O R M A N T . H . S
. I . N . I . D
D . O . D I P L O M A
E . N . L . O . C . D
C H I V E . D A T U M
O . C . . E . O . I
R I S E . E S P R I T
```

54

```
F O R G E T M E N O T
A . A . A . E . A . E
N I G E R I A . I . M
. . . T . S Y R U P
B O U G H . U . O . E
O . N . E . R . B . R
T . C . N . E D I T S
A G L O W . M
N . E . A S E P T I C
I . A . R . N . H . A
C O N T E N T M E N T
```

55

```
W O R L D C L A S S
O . . . U . O . A
R I L L S . L U C C A
M . O . T . L . R . M
S U N S E T . D I V A
. G . D . E . L
L E I A . A D V E R B
I . T . S . I . G . E
V A U N T . S H E A F
. D . E . O . . O
. S E G M E N T I N G
```

56

```
E . B O M B S H E L L
I C E . I . I X . I
F . E A S Y G O I N G
F . C . N . L . H
E X P L O S I V E . T
L . N . F . . H
T . M A S T I C A T E
O . O . T . C . . A
W A T E R F A L L . D
E . I . U . N . E Y E
R E F L E C T E D . D
```

57

```
D E F E C T I O N . M
R . A . O . N . A L E
E D D I N G T O N . L
A . E . S . E . . O
D . S E P A R A T E D
N . . . I . R . I
O F F I C I O U S . O
U . . U . G . W . U
G . A N O M A L O U S
H A M . U . T . R . L
T . Y E S T E R D A Y
```

58

```
P R O F U N D I T Y
. I . U . N . A
E V E N . C L A M P S
. I . D . R . P
M E A S L Y . T H A W
. R . . . . N
R A M P . R E M O T E
. A . O . A . E
C O B W E B . S E N T
. H . E . K . N
. M A D A G A S C A R
```

59

```
A L S A C E . E D A M
L . P . O . E . E
B A R O N . C A P E S
U . E . S . A . R . S
S T A R T U P . I . Y
. . D . R . A . V
R E . U N C L A S P
I . A . E . I T E
D E G A S . T R I P E
E . L . O . O . P
S K E W . G R I N D S
```

60

```
. E M B A R K E D
. O . I . N . E
A I D E D . O F F E R
U . E . S . L . E
D E M O . F L O R A L
I . . W . S . E
T A C T I C . K E E N
O . U . E . R . V . T
R E B E L . E P I C S
. E . D . A . C
. D I S C R E T E
```

Solutions

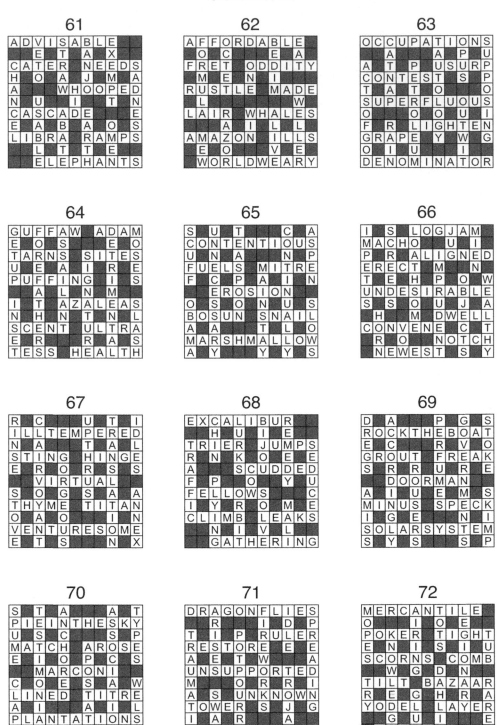

61

A	D	V	I	S	A	B	L	E		
	E		T		A	X				
C	A	T	E	R		N	E	E	D	S
H		O	A	J	M		A			
A			W	H	O	O	P	E	D	
N		U		I		T			N	
C	A	S	C	A	D	E			E	
E		A	B		A	O			S	
L	I	B	R	A		R	A	M	P	S
		L		T		T	E			
E	L	E	P	H	A	N	T	S		

62

A	F	F	O	R	D	A	B	L	E	
	O		C		E	A		A		
F	R	E	T		O	D	D	I	T	Y
	M		E	N	I			I		
R	U	S	T	L	E		M	A	D	E
	L			W						
L	A	I	R		W	H	A	L	E	S
		A		I	L	L				
A	M	A	Z	O	N		I	L	L	S
	E		O		V	E				
W	O	R	L	D	W	E	A	R	Y	

63

O	C	C	U	P	A	T	I	O	N	S
	A		A		A	P		U		
A	T		P		U	S	U	R	P	
C	O	N	T	E	S	T		S		P
T		A		T		O				O
S	U	P	E	R	F	L	U	O	U	S
O			O		O	U		I		
F		R		L	I	G	H	T	E	N
G	R	A	P	E		Y		W		G
O		I		U				I		
D	E	N	O	M	I	N	A	T	O	R

64

G	U	F	F	A	W		A	D	A	M
E		O		S		E		O		O
T	A	R	N	S		S	I	T	E	S
U		A		I		R		E		
P	U	F	F	I	N	G		I		S
	A		L		N	M				
I		T		A	Z	A	L	E	A	S
N	H		T		N	L				
S	C	E	N	T		U	L	T	R	A
E		R		R		A				S
T	E	S	S		H	E	A	L	T	H

65

S	U	T		C		A				
C	O	N	T	E	N	T	I	O	U	S
U		N		A		N		P		
F	U	E	L	S		M	I	T	R	E
F		C		P		A		I		N
	E	R	O	S	I	O	N			
O		S		O		N	U	S		
B	O	S	U	N		S	N	A	I	L
A		A		T			L	O		O
M	A	R	S	H	M	A	L	L	O	W
A		Y			Y			Y		S

66

I	S		L	O	G	J	A	M		
M	A	C	H	O		U		I		
P	R		A	L	I	G	N	E	D	
E	R	E	C	T		M		N		
T		H		P		O		W		
U	N	D	E	S	I	R	A	B	L	E
S	S		S		O		U	J		A
	H		M			D	W	E	L	L
C	O	N	V	E	N	E		C		T
	R		O			N	O	T	C	H
N	E	W	E	S	T		S		Y	

67

R		C			U		T		I	
I	L	L	T	E	M	P	E	R	E	D
N		A			T		A		L	
S	T	I	N	G		H	I	N	G	E
E		R		O	R	S			S	
		V	I	R	T	U	A	L		
S	O		G		S		A		A	
T	H	Y	M	E		T	I	T	A	N
O		A		O		I			I	
V	E	N	T	U	R	E	S	O	M	E
E		T		S					N	X

68

E	X	C	A	L	I	B	U	R		
	H		U		I		E			
T	R	I	E	R		J	U	M	P	S
R		N	K		O	E		E		
A			S	C	U	D	D	E	D	
F		P		O		Y		U		
F	E	L	L	O	W	S			C	
I		Y		R		O		M	E	
C	L	I	M	B		L	E	A	K	S
	N			I		V		L		
	G	A	T	H	E	R	I	N	G	

69

D		A		P		G		S		
R	O	C	K	T	H	E	B	O	A	T
E		C			R		V		O	
G	R	O	U	T		F	R	E	A	K
S		R		R	U	R		E		
	D	O	O	R	M	A	N			
A		I		U	E		M		S	
M	I	N	U	S		S	P	E	C	K
I		G		E			N		N	I
S	O	L	A	R	S	Y	S	T	E	M
S		Y		S				S		P

70

S		T		A			A		T	
P	I	E	I	N	T	H	E	S	K	Y
U		S		C			S		P	
M	A	T	C	H		A	R	O	S	E
E		I		O		P	C		S	
	M	A	R	C	O	N	I			
C		O		E	S	A		W		
L	I	N	E	D		T	I	T	R	E
A			I			I		A		
P	L	A	N	T	A	T	I	O	N	S
S			L			E		N		H

71

D	R	A	G	O	N	F	L	I	E	S
	R			I		D		P		
T	I	P		R	U	L	E	R		
R	E	S	T	O	R	E		E	E	
A		E		T		W		A		
U	N	S	U	P	P	O	R	T	E	D
M			O		R	R		I		
A		S		U	N	K	N	O	W	N
T	O	W	E	R		S		J		G
I		A	R				A			
C	O	N	T	I	N	G	E	N	C	Y

72

M	E	R	C	A	N	T	I	L	E	
O			I		O	E				
P	O	K	E	R		T	I	G	H	T
E		N		I		S		I		U
S	C	O	R	N	S		C	O	M	B
		W		G		D		N		
T	I	L	T		B	A	Z	A	A	R
R		E		G		H		R		A
Y	O	D	E	L		L	A	Y	E	R
		G		U		I				E
B	E	N	E	F	A	C	T	O	R	

Solutions

73

```
CURRICULUM
 K   O  A I
FUND BLURRY
 L  E  U  G
BELONG HOOK
 L       P
BEES ZENITH
   C  I E I
UPKEEP SUMS
 A  N   T A
NEEDLESSLY
```

74

```
 ACERBITY
 A  E C E
THIRD AWARD
A R O R R I
FOOD TUSSLE
F   A  S  T
EASILY ASIA
T A K N P R
AORTA EBONY
  I L A O
 SLIPPERY
```

75

```
DEACTIVATED
  P    I A E
MR O NICKS
EVOLVED T I
L N E I G
OBSTRUCTION
D  W  A M A
R Z HOTSPOT
ALIKE E A E
M  N  L  L
ACCOMMODATE
```

76

```
P   DESERTS
RELY  A E K
E A A F PLY
T MACHETE S
E E C G N C
NONSEQUITUR
T T S A A A
I ALSORAN P
ORB I D C E
U L O TEAR
STERNUM   S
```

77

```
C HAMBURGER
AGO A P L E
R POSITIONS
N  T  O S P
INCREASES L
V  R  C   E
O APPORTION
R C I A   D
ORCHESTRA E
U R C C MEN
SPACESHIP T
```

78

```
P  ACCRUED
RATS A N O
E R E P DIM
V ALLTIME I
A N I L R N
RESEMBLANCE
I I I A E E
C SANGRIA R
ART A Y T I
T O T  THIN
EERIEST   G
```

79

```
C I COFFER
HOSTA  E U
A S FAWNING
LOUSE  H G
I I T I V H
CONCENTRATE
E G R E C A
 V  I FAULT
PITFALL I E
 E A  AFTER
WAXING Y S
```

80

```
D  CHIMERA
IONS N X R
S A E F PER
C TAXFREE A
O U P I R N
UNRELENTING
R A I G E E
A LECTERN M
GIG A S C E
E A T  TEEN
DISCERN   T
```

81

```
 E BROILER
LUCRE  C E
 O DEFECTS
MINOR  D T
O O O S O L
COMFORTABLE
C Y M R T S
A  S  OPALS
SENEGAL  I
I  A  LANES
NUCLEUS  S
```

82

```
FUNCTIONARY
 O   B W  E
BRP SYRIA
ARMREST Y R
C A R I   B
KILIMANJARO
P  A A M  O
E S NITPICK
DANCE E D S
A  A  N   S
LIGHTFOOTED
```

83

```
P  FINESSE
ALAS O T X
R UP M RAP
T CORSICA L
I T O N I O
CLIFFHANGER
I O E T H A
P NASCENT T
ACE S S E I
T E O ONTO N
EARDRUM   N
```

84

```
PIPEDREAM
 I R  L A
KENYA ENDOW
I E M G A A
B  ABYSMAL
B G U  E L
UNLEASH  A
T Y B E M B
ZIPPY NOISY
 H S C N
SUSPENDED
```

Solutions

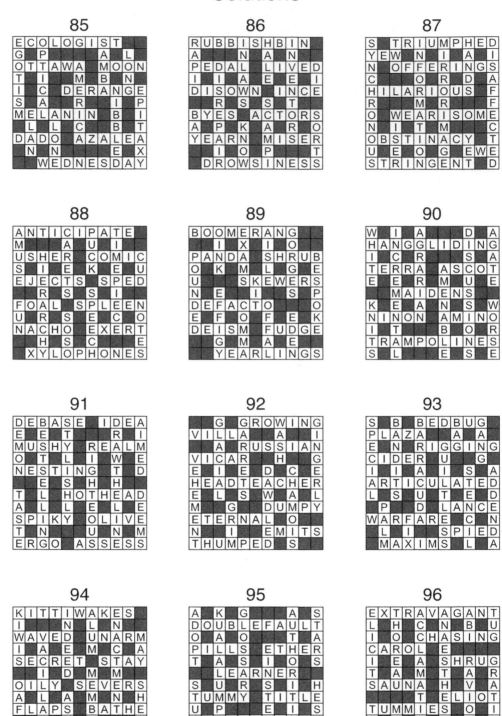

85

ECOLOGIST
OTTAWA MOON
DERANGE
MELANIN
DADO AZALEA
WEDNESDAY

86

RUBBISHBIN
PEDAL LIVED
DISOWN INCE
BYES ACTORS
YEARN MISER
DROWSINESS

87

S TRIUMPHED
OFFERINGS
HILARIOUS
WEARISOME
OBSTINACY
STRINGENT

88

ANTICIPATE
USHER COMIC
EJECTS SPED
FOAL SPLEEN
NACHO EXERT
XYLOPHONES

89

BOOMERANG
PANDA SHRUB
SKEWERS
DEFACTO
DEISM FUDGE
YEARLINGS

90

HANGGLIDING
TERRA ASCOT
MAIDENS
NINON AMINO
TRAMPOLINES

91

DEBASE IDEA
MUSHY REALM
NESTING
HOTHEAD
SPIKY OLIVE
ERGO ASSESS

92

G GROWING
VILLA
RUSSIAN
VICAR
HEADTEACHER
DUMPY
ETERNAL
EMITS
THUMPED

93

S B BEDBUG
PLAZA
RIGGING
CIDER
ARTICULATED
P D LANCE
WARFARE
SPIED
MAXIMS

94

KITTIWAKES
WAVED UNARM
SECRET STAY
OILY SEVERS
FLAPS BATHE
CENSORSHIP

95

A K G A S
DOUBLEFAULT
PILLS ETHER
LEARNER
TUMMY TITLE
CRUMBLINESS

96

EXTRAVAGANT
CHASING
CAROL
SHRUG
SAUNA
ELIOT
TUMMIES
MOMENTARILY

Solutions

97

	S	A	D	M	I	R	E	S
D	O	T	E	D		B		O
	A		D	O	L	E	F	U	L
D	I	N	E	R		X		O
E		D	E		H	C	I	
A	M	B	A	S	S	A	D	O	R	S
D	Y		S		R	L	T	
L		I		D	O	O	M	S
I	S	O	T	O	P	E		G
N		C		S	I	N	G	S
E	N	C	H	A	N	T		E

98

| S | | G | U | A | T | E | M | A | L | A |
|P|R|Y| |G| |X| |S| |N|
|R| |M|I|G|R|A|T|I|O|N|
|I| |R| |R|M|D|I| |V|
|N|E|C|T|A|R|I|N|E| |E|
|G| | |V| |N| | |E|
|F| |C|H|A|R|A|C|T|E|R|
|I| |R| |T| |T| |S|
|E|X|A|M|I|N|I|N|G| |A|
|L| |W| |N| |O| |E|R|R|
|D|I|L|I|G|E|N|C|E| |Y|

99

F	O	R	E	S	I	G	H	T
	A		A		E		E
S	W	I	R	L		C	O	N	E	S
M		L	S	K	D	K
U		A	P	O	L	O	G	Y
D		P	I	N		L
G	A	L	L	O	P	S		I
E		A	X		T	D		N
S	P	I	L	L		E	L	U	D	E
N		I	E	K
S	U	P	E	R	S	E	D	E

100

101

102

103

104

105

106

107

108

Solutions

109

```
F O L L O W E R
  L   E   I   E
H E D G E   G A T E S
O   E   K   W   R   C
T E R N   P A G O D A
D     R   M     L
O R A T O R   C H A D
G   R   U   O   O   E
S C O O T   H I R E D
  M   E   M   D
  A S S I S T E D
```

110

```
B O R E R S   S M O G
E   E   E     O   I
L A S T S   R O U N D
T   T   O   E   N   D
S H R O U D S   T   Y
  I   R   U   A
V   C   C E R T I F Y
I   T   E   F   N   A
S H I N S   A M O U R
I   O     C   U   N
T O N E   M E S S E S
```

111

```
A   H A R V E S T E D
G N U   E   G   H   I
O   M E C H A N I C S
R     T   L   N   Q
A P P E A R I N G   U
P     N   T     I
H   R I G M A R O L E
O   O   U   R     T
B A L A L A I K A   I
I   L   A   A   G I N
A S S U R A N C E   G
```

112

```
C A N D E S C E N T
  L   O   I   O
S L O W   M I G H T Y
  E   S   R   H
E G R E S S   T U S K
  R           N
W O R M   B A M B O O
  I   Y   A   R
F I D D L E   L I K E
  O   S     T   E
  N O T I C E A B L E
```

113

```
P   H E R E T I C
L E A F   E   Y   U
E   S   C   S   P E T
A   S C A L E N E   A
S   O   V   N   W   N
U N C H A R T E R E D
R   I   L   F   I   D
A   A C C O U N T   R
B A T   A   L   E   I
L   E D   T R U E   I
E N D L E S S     D
```

114

```
S   U   P   F   B
C O N T A M I N A T E
O   I   F   S   A
R U F F S   F A C E S
E   I   E   L   I   T
  C A P T I O N
F   A   A   N   A   M
L A T E R   G U T S Y
U   I   A     I   R
F R O N T R U N N E R
F   N   E   G   H
```

115

```
C H U R C H M A N
  N   O   I   E
F E I G N   D I C E D
U   T   G   G   T   E
R     O V E R A L L
L   A   I   R   A
O U T C O M E   Y
N   H   A   G   O   E
G U E S S   G L U E D
  N   E   E   Z
  A S S I D U O U S
```

116

```
O   B   B A F F L E
S P A C E   U   U
T   B   L I B R A R Y
R O Y A L   A   O
I   S   I   N   I L
C O I N C I D E N C E
H   T   O   S   H   N
  F     S   T W A N G
T E M P E R A   B   T
  E   O   N E I G H
L O D G E D   T   Y
```

117

```
L I M I T A T I O N
O     I   E   V
T A P E D   S H E L F
U   U   T   R   O
S E P T E T   A J A R
  P   D   D   O
A G E S   P R A Y E D
N   T   R   E   E   A
T H E T A   A D D E R
  E   I   M     E
  T R A D I T I O N S
```

118

```
L E V E L H E A D E D
I   E   A   L   I   W
T E X T U R E   S   I
    G   P I T O N
C A T C H   H   U   D
O   U   I   A   R   L
N   N   N   N O B L E
D O I N G   T
U   S   G R I S T L E
C   I   A   N   O   N
T R A N S F E R R E D
```

119

```
A   I     I Q   J
M A N U F A C T U R E
I   F   E   A   W
T W I N E   C A N O E
Y   L   M   R   T   L
    T A B L E A U
S   R   O   A   M   C
L E A D S   M U L C H
E   T   S     E
P R E M E D I T A T E
T   D   D     P K
```

120

```
C A P A B I L I T Y
O   U   I   E
W I P E R   S H R E W
E   E D   T   R   E
D A N C E D   R I T E
  E   N   F   F
J U T E   B E L I E F
I   R   T   E   E   R
B L A D E   B A D L Y
  T   N   L     U
G E T T H E C H O P
```

Solutions

121

```
HALFTRUTH D
O  O  R  T  URE
SUBMARINE  F
P  E  N  L    E
I  SUSPICION
T     P  T    C
ASTRONAUT  E
L     R  R  R L
I  ATTRIBUTE E
TAX  E  A  C  S
Y  ENDANGERS
```

122

```
BABOON  CHAP
A  R  V    I  R
TRIBE  FUGUE
C  L  R  R  HS
HOLIDAY  W  S
   I  R  I  A
Q  A  ANNOYED
U  N  W  G  C O
ANTON  PROUD
L  L     A  D O
MOYA  INFERS
```

123

```
BELT  UNUSED
E  E     E  E  E
VEGAN  MINES
E  E     E  A  TK
L  R  GATHERS
      D  O     N
PLEATED  T  W
O  M  I  E     A
KOALA  SHOPS
E  I  T     U  P
DENIED  ASKS
```

124

```
AMELIORATES
   N     E  U U
V  J  P  SAFER
APOSTLE  T  V
C  I  E  R     E
CONTROVERSY
I     O  O  E  I
N  R  STILTON
ARENA  R  U  G
T  A  U     R
EXPERIMENTS
```

125

```
ECCENTRIC
   O  E  I  H
TOPIC  ORION
R  E  K  J  N E
I     SPATULA
P  P  U  P     R
OBLONGS     E
D  A  O  A  L S
SWIFT  TWIST
   C  E  Y  O
   ENDURANCE
```

126

```
WORDPERFECT
I  A  E  E  N E
GENERIC  D  A
      A  OBOES
BESOM  G  R  E
U  P  B  N  S R
CANAL  I  IDEAS
C     L  T
H  O  ARIZONA
E  F  T  O  L W
RAFAELNADAL
```

127

```
BADTEMPERED
   O     E  A  I
D  Z  O  ROVER
EXEMPTS  E  E
C  N  P  E     C
ABSTRACTART
T     E  U  G  I
H  K  SITDOWN
LAIRS  E  U  G
O  E  O     T
NEVERENDING
```

128

```
HOMEOSTASIS
U  O  V  R  A O
S  L  EXACTLY
TILER  N     T
L  U  B  STRUT
E  S  E  P  E O
DACHA  A  C  P
      R  RILED
ROUTINE  A  O
E  M  N  N  I W
DRAUGHTSMAN
```

129

```
REVERENCE
E  I     R  R
GENEVA  IRIS
A  T  R  S  D
L  A  STOPPER
I  G     I  I
AGELESS  A  P
   U  O  T  N O
FROG  SCOOPS
   U  O     L T
   ASPARTAME
```

130

```
O  A     E  C W
WORDOFMOUTH
N  C     P  T I
ETHOS  EXTOL
R  I  E  R  I E
   PURLOIN
E  E  P  R  G P
VALVE  STEEL
I  A  N     D A
LIGHTWEIGHT
S  O  S     E E
```

131

```
P  S  P     S  A
INTERRUPTED
S  A  E     A  I
TITUS  CARGO
E  E  E  H  S S
   LARGEST
W  Y  V  R  U C
OCHRE  RIDER
R  O     I  D A
REMORSELESS
Y  E     S  D H
```

132

```
D     GLANCED
INCH  B  O  O
S  H  C  S  MAW
I  ROOFTOP  N
N  O  L  A  H
CONSOLIDATE
L  I  N  N  I A
I  CONCERN  R
NIL  A  D  E T
E  E  D  EDGE
DESCENT     D
```

Solutions

133
```
P L E N T I F U L
R   I   A   I
T H R O B   I O N I C
R   S   I   T   E A
O     A S H T R A Y
D   S   L     S   E
D E P L O Y S     N
E   A   U   T   P N
N E W T S   O P I N E
    N   T   L   N
    S U S P E C T E D
```

134
```
U     I N F U S E S   S
N A P S   O   I   U
D   A   S   U   D I P
E   R E T I N U E   P
R   A   T   W   O
S A G I T T A R I U S
T   R   I   N   I
A   A D O R N E D   T
T O P   N   S   E   I
E   H E   D R N O   N
D E S I R E S       N
```

135
```
E S T A B L I S H
L     A   E     E
A L L O U T   N E W T
S   L   I   S   E
T   E   U N L E A R N
I   S   G   U   A
C A T W A L K   S   R
  N   A   E   T   R
S T U D   S I E R R A
  S   E       I   T
    P R O P A G A T E
```

136
```
O   S   E       C   L
D O C U M E N T A R Y
D   R   B   R   R
L A U R A   B E T T E
Y   M   T   L   O   S
    P U T T I N G
S   T   L   S   R   W
C H I L E   S T A K E
A   O   F   P   E
L O U D M O U T H E D
E   S   L   Y   S
```

137
```
B A C K T O B A C K
E   A   A   H
L E A R N   G A I T S
L   N   D S E   K
Y O N D E R   I F F Y
  A   M   F   T
L I P S   A R M A D A
E   U   W   A I   M
T E R S E   M A N G O
  N   A   E       N
V A R N I S H I N G
```

138
```
R E F U S E   D I S C
A   O   K   N   A
N E R V Y   F E V E R
G   G   D   A   P
E D I T I O N   L   S
    V   V   A   U
M   E   I N T E N T S
A   N   N   I T   H
C L E G G   C H A I R
R   S   A   R   E
O A S T   P L A Y E D
```

139
```
A   S U I T C A S E S
T A P   L   O   A   C
R   A L L I G A T O R
O   U   N   E
C R O S S W O R D   W
I   T   S       D
O   A U R I C U L A R
U   M   A   E   I
S U B S T A N C E   V
L   E   E T   L I E
Y A R D S T I C K   R
```

140
```
  A   G R E A S E S
Y U C C A   M   E
  T   T W E E T E R
C R U D E   N   E
H A W L F N
U L T R A M A R I N E
R E   Y U C L
N   H   N U T T Y
I N C I T E D   I
N   L   E L V E S
G L I T T E R   E
```

141
```
  I M M O D E S T
    I   G   N   R
M A N O R   A M E N D
U   E   E C N   R
F O R T   S T A D I A
F   C   S       G
L I V E R Y   S W A G
E   A   A T E   E
R A N G Y   W A D E D
  E   O   E G
  S U N D E R E D
```

142
```
    S   T E M P L E S
C O C K Y   E   O
    O   P R O G R A M
C O U T H   S   B
R R O B B   B R
A G G L O M E R A T E
S E N S N R
H   B   I D A H O   N
I N D E X E D   N
N   A   E V A D E
G R O U N D S   S
```

143
```
A   E P   F   E
B O X E R S H O R T S
D   P E   I   S
U N L I T   B U G L E
L   I   E   L H X
  C O N D U I T
C A D E E K
O A T H S   C A N O N
U   I   H I E
P R O V I S I O N A L
E N   P G T
```

144
```
  S T I T C H E S
  A   U   I   I
K E B A B   R I G I D
N O A I N E
I R O N   U N I S O N
T   V G I
T I D I E S   Y O G A
E O S O C L
R A G E S   B E E P S
  M E E A
  A L L A Y I N G
```

Solutions

145

```
L U M B E R J A C K
E   N     O   R
E S H E R   H E I D I
D   A   O   N   T   N
S A L M O N   D E C K
    F   T   S   R
Y O D A   R A D I A L
A   O   Y   M   O   A
M E Z Z O   P A N S Y
  E   G   L       B
  I N D I R E C T L Y
```

146

```
C A D R E S   D A M P
O   E   M     N   A
V A C U A   M O T O R
E   O   C   A   E   R
N U R S I N G   C   Y
    A   A   N   H
V   T   T H E M A S K
O   I   E   S   M   N
C L O U D   I M B U E
A   N     U   E   L
L E S S   A M O R A L
```

147

```
D I S S I P A T I O N
I   E   N   R   N   E
D E C L A I M   D   A
    T   E R U P T   L
S H E E T   D   L   E
L   X   E   F   G   N
A   P   N   O P E N S
P L E A T   R
P   P   N   I N C E N S E
E   D   V   E   A   V
D I S P E N S A B L E
```

148

149

150

151

152

153

154

```
B R E A D C R U M B
  E   C     R   I
M E S H   D E B U T S
  N   E   I   A
L A P D O G   N U T S
  C           O
S T O P   W A T E R Y
    R   O   R   M
A V I A T E   A P E D
  I   W     W   N
  A N N I H I L A T E
```

155

```
P   A   L A W F U L
H Y D R A   E   U
Y   J   S N O W I N G
S H O R T   R   G
I   U   D   I N   C
C A R D I O G R A P H
S   N   T   I R   A
  U   C   N O W I N
T R A C H E A   H   N
  N   O     T R A C E
  S U B D U E   L   L
```

156

```
I N T E N T I O N A L
L   U   E   N   U   A
K I T T E N S   R   W
    D   T A T T Y
A U R A L   I   U   E
I   E   E   N   R
R   M   P   C H E F S
D U O M O   T
R   V   I N I T I A L
O   A   N   V   L   U
P U L L T H E P L U G
```

Solutions

157

```
S E D U C E   S C A N
A   I   H     O   O
V I S T A   E N N I S
E   T   T   N   S   E
S T R E T C H   I   S
    I   E A D
C   B   R U N N E R S
L   U   E   C   R   E
A S T E R   I M A G E
I   E       N   T   R
M I D I   E G R E T S
```

158

```
A   B     M   D   B
C R E D I B I L I T Y
T   D     N   C   L
O B E Y S   E X T R A
R   V   U   R   A   W
    I M P L A N T
P   L   E   L   O   A
L E M U R   S C R U B
U   E   M       I   E
C O N T A M I N A N T
K   T   N       L   S
```

159

```
B O D E G A   L I M B
U   I   E     N   U
M A S O N   O L D E N
P   C   E   V   I   N
S T O R A G E   F   Y
    V   L   R   F
S   E   O Y S T E R S
T   R   G   I   R   W
U N I F Y   G E E S E
F   N       H   N   A
F O G S   S T A T O R
```

160

```
    F   B U I L D U P
V O L G A   O   R
    O   L U M B A G O
V I T A L   S   P
I   S   A   H   T   E
G R A N D F A T H E R
O   M   S   N   E   T
R   S   D E R B Y
O R A C L E S   M
U   A   E L A N D
S C A R L E T   L
```

161

```
S P E C T A C U L A R
O   A   O   O   I   E
P U R S U E R   A   V
    R   N O I S E   T
A H E A D   S   R   T
R   X   E   R   O   T
C   P   F   S I N K S
H E L L O   T
A   A   R H O M B U S
I   I   C   N   A   A
C O N F E D E R A C Y
```

162

```
    R   C O A S T E R
S K U L L   K     E
    C   A S P I R I N
C I T E S   M     O
O   I   S   V   M U
C O O P E R A T I O N
O   N   S   C   C   C
N   B   A G R E E
U N Q U I E T   O
T   R   E L B O W
S C E N T E D   E
```

163

```
I N D I V I S I B L E
    I   M   R   N
P A U   A X I N G
O R D I N A L   M   R
R   E   H   L   O
T E M P E S T U O U S
F   A   A   P   S
O   S   R E L A P S E
L U C I D   K   U D
I   U   O       G
O U T O F B O U N D S
```

164

```
S   U   S   W   S
C O N S T I T U E N T
A   D   U   L   E
R E E D S   B A L S A
Y   R   Q B M K
    G L U C O S E
S   R   A R A T   T
A L O U D   N A N C Y
U   U   R   I   P
C O N C O R D A N C E
E   D   N   G   D
```

165

```
    I D E A L I S M
    I   L   G   E
B R E W S   L I L A C
L   G   O   O   T   L
U P O N   M O U S S E
R   C   S       A
R E D H O T   A M I R
E   I   R   B   A   L
D I V E S   A L L E Y
    A   E   L   L
    N O T E L E S S
```

166

```
S   I   E O   K
C O N C E I V A B L E
A   H   I   S   M
R E A D S   C R E E P
S   B   M   T   S   T
    I V O R I E S
P   T   O   N   I P
R E A C T   G A V E L
I   N   H   E   E A
D E C E I T F U L L Y
E   Y   E   Y   S
```

167

```
  C H E R U B I C
    U   O   A   U
N A M E D   B E B O P
A   A   S   I   I   O
M O N K   M E N T A L
I   B   S       E
B O D K I N   C R A M
I   E   K   U   I
A L I B I   D O R I C
    S   N   D   A
    T R I C Y C L E
```

168

```
E T C H   T R I C K S
L   O     E   A   L
D I N G Y   S C U B A
E   D   A   P   L   N
R   I   C L O S I N G
    T   H   N   F
H O I S T E D   L   S
A   O   S   E   O L
V E N O M   D O W N Y
O   E   A       E L
C O R O N A   T R A Y
```

Solutions

169

170

171

172

173

174

175

176

177

178

179

180

Solutions

181

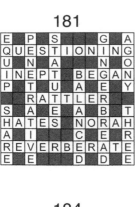

```
E P S . . G A
Q U E S T I O N I N G
U . N . A . N . O
I N E P T . B E G A N
P . T . U . A . E . Y
. . R A T T L E R . .
S . A . E . A . B . T
H A T E S . N O R A H
A . I . . . C . E . R
R E V E R B E R A T E
E . E . . . D . D . E
```

182

```
B L U E B O T T L E
O . U . E . I
G U S T Y . A L B U M
U . E . I . S . E . O
S E V E N S . B R E W
. E . G . F . A
H U N T . D I C T U M
I . T . S . S . E . I
T W E A K . H O S T S
. E . . Y . E . S
U N D E R S T U D Y
```

183

```
D I D G E R I D O O
. G . R . . O . F
U N D O . C O D I F Y
. O . . S . O . G
C R U S T Y . E P E E
. E . . . . . . N
A D D S . U P P I T Y
. N . . S . R . R
I G U A N A . E R A S
. A . . G . E . N
P A S S I O N A T E
```

184

```
E . S . T . . B . B
D O M E S T I C A T E
G . A . U . N . S
E L L E N . A N K L E
R . L . A . B . H . T
. . M E M E N T O . .
T . I . I . E . L . R
W I N E S . G R I P E
I . D . A . D . E
C R E D E N T I A L S
E . D . . . E . Y . E
```

185

```
U N O B S E R V A N T
. C . . E . V . U
E U P . C H E E R . N
V A L A N C E . R . S
A . A . E . S . S . S
C I R C U M S P E C T
U . M . . I . A . I
A D . A R O U S A L .
T A U N T . N E E .
E . L . I . . . L
D E L I C I O U S L Y
```

186

```
C . C H R Y S A L I S
L E A . E . T . I . E
E . R E M B R A N D T
A . . O . O . K . T . L
R U M I N A N T S . L
H . . S . G . . . E
E . C Y T O P L A S M
A . A . R . O . . . N
D O G M A T I S M . N
E . E . T . N . A C T
D I S S E C T E D . S
```

187

```
M O N U M E N T S . .
. E . O . I . E
U N C U T . C L A S P
N . K . T . H . M . E
E . . O P E N A I R .
Q . A . A . N . . . T
U N K E M P T . . . U
A . I . A . U . P . R
L A M B S . B L U R B
. B . T . E . P
. O B S E R V A N T
```

188

```
D I S B E L I E V E R
. U . . N . A . A
W . B G . T E S T S .
H A U T E U R . E . P
I . R . N . I . . . B
S U B S T A N T I V E
P . L . S . N . R
E . H . E M I T T E R
R E A R M . C . E . Y
E . U . E . . . R
D E L I N Q U E N C Y
```

189

```
R E P A I D . C U F F
O . R . N . . N . A
B R E A D . C U P I D
E . C . E . H . A . E
S W I M M E R . L . D
. . P . N . O . A
F . I . I G N I T E D
I . T . T . I . A . O
G L O R Y . C A B L E
H . U . . . L . L . R
T O S S . J E W E L S
```

190

```
S . I . . M . S . S
C O M P E T I T I O N
A . P . . G . L . A
L E E K S . R I V E R
D . R . I . A . E . K
. . M O N I T O R . .
S . E . I . E . M . P
P R A M S . S T E A L
O . B . T . . . D . I
K I L L E R W H A L E
E . E . R . . . L . D
```

191

```
C O M M E N D A B L E
. I . . E . O . M
D L P . S N O O P . .
E L I T I S T . K . L
A . E . S . R . . . O
T R U S T W O R T H Y
H . A . Y . H . E . .
T . B . C H E M I S E
R O U G H . R . E . S
A . R . I . . . V
P U R P O S E L E S S
```

192

```
D I S T I N C T I O N
O . E . N . O . C . O
N E W B O R N . E . S
. . . F . N A C R E .
G R I E F . O . O . G
L . N . E . I . L . A
I . E . N . S A D L Y
D A R T S . S
E . T . I C E B E R G
R . I . V . U . G . E
S T A G E F R I G H T
```

Solutions

193

```
S T M . . D . I
P R E P A R A T I O N
I . R . N . . S D
N O M A D . M A I Z E
S . I . A . E L . X
. N A T U R A L
A . A . E . C U . S
F E T E S . H A S T E
F . I . A . I U
I G N O M I N I O U S
X . G . . T . N S
```

194

```
S U P P R E S S E D
. P . O . . M U
C H A R . P I A N O S
. E . C . E S
C A S H E W . H I R E
. V . . . O
L E G S . J A U N T S
. . C A N . A
A D O R E R . C I T Y
. A . A . L . E
D I M I N U E N D O
```

195

```
R E P U G N A N C E
A . L . R . O
I N D I A . M O N T H
D . E . Z . S C . A
S O O N E R . G O N G
. . D . D . S . U
H O O F . U N T R U E
O . R . S . I . S L
G U A V A . T H E M E
. N . G . C . C
A T T A C H M E N T
```

196

```
B U E N O S A I R E S
O . R . P . E . A
B U G B E A R . D N
. . N . O V O I D
F A U N A . D . P . I
A . R . N . Y . N I
N U D . N I G H T
A E G I S . A
T . U . H A M M O C K
I . A . U . I . W E
C R Y P T I C A L L Y
```

197

```
S M O O T H E D
. O U . A . R
M A L E S . I C I N G
E . A . T . R E . E
L A R K . O D D S O N
O . P . O . T
D E F E A T . W A V E
I . U . E . T D . E
C A M E L . A V A I L
. E . L . P
S T A C C A T O
```

198

```
T R E N D Y . A Q U A
A . F . I . . U . N
C A F E S . U N I O N
I . E . P . N . C . O
T I C K L E S . K . Y
. T . A . E . W
D . I . Y E L L I N G
O . V . E . F . T . E
D R E A D . I N T E R
G . L . . S . E . M
Y O Y O . S H A D E S
```

199

```
D I Z Z I N E S S
I . A . . W . V
S I M P L E . O X E N
A . B . X . O . I
V E . S P I N D L E
O . Z . O . . I . R
W H I T E S T . C . R
. A . A . E . T . A
R I N K . D E S I G N
. R . E . . O . D
W R A P P I N G S
```

200

```
A . C . . T U . N
S H O R T C H A N G E
S . R . . R . C . W
A R R A Y . E L O P E
Y . O . O . S . N . R
. B L U S H E S
C . O . T . E . C . S
H A R S H . D R I N K
U . A . F . . O . A
C I T R U S F R U I T
K . E . L . . S . E
```

201

```
. P . A Z I M U T H
B E L I E . O . . E
. A . R O M A N I A
M I C R O . T . . V
E . A . B . A . B . Y
N O T H I N G N E S S
I . E . C . A . G . E
S . O . . I N G O T
C A R R Y O N . A
U . A . . S O R R Y
S E L L O U T S . S
```

202

```
A B B R E V I A T E D
D U . M . N . H . I
O M N I B U S . U . O
. . A . T E N O R
L A S E R . R . D . A
A . U . R . U E . M
M M A . C U R I A
B E A D S . T
A . T . S T I F F E N
D . R . E . O . O . I
A B A N D O N M E N T
```

203

```
A . M . . R O . E
B E A C H C O M B E R
O . G . . L . S . A
U N I T S . L I E N S
T . S . O . O . R . E
. T E L A V I V
S . E . U . E . A . B
W O R S T . R O T O R
I . I . . I . O . I
P L A Y O N W O R D S
E . L . N . . Y . K
```

204

```
. C O R R I D O R
. R . U . R . I
J A D E D . E L V I S
A . E . D . A . A . H
N O R M . I M E L D A
U . S . S . S . M
A N G E L S . C H U B
R . R . I . A . A . L
Y I E L D . B I L G E
. B . E . L . T
E S S A Y I S T
```

Solutions

205

206

207

208

209

210

211

212

213

214

215

216

Solutions

217

```
CALIBRATE
L E     O   K
ENTRAP XRAY
A T   R I L
R U PUNCHED
U C   D E   R
PREMIER A A
  I A N R C
CORD THATCH
  T L     E M
  PYROMANIA
```

218

```
CAVA FLOATS
A I     A S E
MANIA UNTIL
P D U N O L
  S I TIDINGS
    C O E   I
CHARMER S B
A T A E H U
BUILT DEIFY
A O I     N E
LUNACY AGAR
```

219

```
A S     T C A
WATERMELONS
A I     A M S
INPUT COPSE
T U O H U T
    LONGEST
W A E R A D
HATED SETTO
I I E     I U
PROSANDCONS
S N F     N E
```

220

```
AGGRIEVED
  A N A R
BURMA GOING
E B N U F O
D   EJECTED
B U O   S L
UPSURGE   I
G H E X J K
SPEAR INURE
  R U T D
  SANDSTONE
```

221

```
SYMPATHETIC
  O E A   O
D T A RIPEN
REISSUE E V
A O C A   E
WONDERFULLY
B R T O   I
A S TREASON
COPRA R E G
K U I   R
STRENUOUSLY
```

222

```
UNSCATHED
N H     N C
SQUIRM VOLE
O T O O A
U O UNDYING
N F O   N R
DEFLECT F A
  X I L   M
LANK ESTEEM
  M E     C A
  ESCALATOR
```

223

```
PERSONAL
  N I A A
STALL SPRIG
T C T S V R
ARTS SAHARA
R F U   N
DESPOT INTO
O I T E L
MURAL OMEGA
  E O L D
NOWADAYS
```

224

```
O S ENAMEL
CRUEL I O
C G ELIXIRS
LOGIC N D
U E T A B U
DISSOLUTION
E T R G K T
  C A UNITY
CRAWLER N I
A A AVIAN
GOSPEL S G
```

225

```
INHABITANTS
R A R R O A
KEYHOLE S I
    A PETAL
TREAD I R O
R X C D I R
A P A ATLAS
SEEKS T
H R TRIGGER
E T E O E I
DISGRUNTLED
```

226
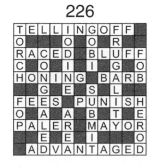
```
TELLINGOFF
O O O R
RACED BLUFF
C O I G O
HONING BARB
  G E S L
FEES PUNISH
O A B T E
PALER MAYOR
  E E I O
ADVANTAGED
```

227

```
  C BELGIUM
SHOVE R I
  R DEMONIC
VERGE W H
O U V M D I
CAPTIVATING
A T L N S A
T U   ARGON
IDYLLIC U
V N LISTS
ENHANCE T
```

228

```
S PROCESSED
COOL N P Y
I TRIATHLON
N V E I A
TOPSECRET M
I B T I
L SARCASTIC
U A I A
APENNINES L
T D C E ALL
EYESHADOW Y
```

Solutions

229

```
S O A P O P E R A . B
I . D . N . L . F E E
T R E N C H A N T . A
T . L . L . B . . U .
I . E C O N O M I S T
N . . U . R . . . I .
G U A R D I A N S . F
D . . N . T . I . U .
U . U N I V E R S A L
C O S . N . L . Q . L
K . E V E R Y B O D Y
```

230

```
. C H A Y W I R E
B R O K E . A . Y .
. E . A N T I Q U E
M I X E R . T . L .
. E . E . A . R . I
D E S C R I P T I O N
. I . T . S . L . B E
C . F . E M B E R
I N D R A W N . O .
N . E . T E N T S
E A G E R L Y . S
```

231

```
B I R T H P L A C E .
I . Y . O . O .
P O S S E . B E L O W
E . T . N . E . O
D U R B A N . L E A N
. A . S . K . C .
D E W S . I N S T E P
O . P . A . O . I
G R O W L . C A D E T
. L . E . K . C
B L A C K S M I T H
```

232

```
S . S . C . . K . A
C O M P O S I T I O N
R . I . R . N . D
A S T I R . T U D O R
P . H E W . H . E
. E N C L O S E .
S . R . T . F . A . S
T R E S S . A R R O W
O . E . C . T . A
C O N C I S E N E S S
K . S . D . D . H
```

233

```
P . R E P O S E D
H O A X . L . A . O
I . S . B U T O W
L . T R O U N C E . N
O . R . D D L . T
S T O R Y T E L L E R
O . N G R I . O
P . O P U L E N T .
H E M . A . R E D
E . I R . I S L E
R E C E D E S . N
```

234

```
R E G I S T R A R .
. I . T . O E
F O R G O . N A M E S
L . L . M . D . A . C
I . . A B O L I S H
P . D . O . N . O
P R E T E X T . L
E . M . A . Y . H . L
D O U B T . I T E M S
. R . E . N . R
E G R E G I O U S
```

235

```
S . M . . M . C . A
T R A C K R E C O R D
A . C . R . N . O
T U R F S . M A J O R
E . O . T . A . U . N
. S T A T I O N
T . C . R . D . C . F
R O O F S . S I T A R
A . P . H . I . A
C R I M I N O L O G Y
T . C . P . . N . S
```

236

```
O . W O R K P L A C E
B O O . E . O W . Y
S . O B F U S C A T E
T . R . S R . C
R E Q U I S I T E . A
U . G . B . T
C . A P E R I O D I C
T . L . R . L . H
I S O L A T I N G . I
V . N . T . T . O W N
E A G L E E Y E D . G
```

237

```
A . P . . N . D . A
F O R T H C O M I N G
O . E . . T . F . I
O A S I S . A W F U L
T . E . W . T . E . E
. N O I S I E R
S . T . M . O . E . S
W E A N S . N I N T H
A . B . U . . C . U
B E L L I G E R E N T
S . E . T . . S . S
```

238

```
D . F . T R O W E L .
I D L E R . E . I
S . U . A C A D E M Y
R O M A N . T . O
U . M . S . T . M . G
P R O H I B I T I O N
T . X . E . T . N . A
. G . N U N D E R
P L A N T E D . F . L
U . O . E D U C E
T O W E R S . L . D
```

239

```
H O T T E M P E R E D
A . O . V . R . I . R
C . R . A W E S O M E
K N O L L . C
S . N . O . I R O N S
A . T . N . P . U .
W R O N G . I T . S
. O . T I D E S
M A J O R C A . O . I
A . U . I . T . O . O
T E T R A H E D R O N
```

240

```
G . . B O R E D O M
O R C A . E . E . A
O . O . A . S . S A G
D . R E G A T T A . N
N . N . G . R . L . A
A F F I R M A T I O N
T . L . E . I . N . I
U . O R G A N Z A . M
R A W . A . T . T . O
E . E . T . M E N U
D A R K E S T . . S
```

Solutions

241

```
 VIEWINGS
  T   A E C
KHAKI GLASS
A L  F A L L
RHYS STAPLE
A   E  E   N
OBTAIN USED
K R  G T L E
EPOCH ODOUR
  T  T R T
 SKYLIGHT
```

242

```
SUSCEPTIBLE
  T   E A  N
EUG EXCEL  I
DUDGEON K  I
U I  N A  G
CHOREOGRAPH
A   R E L T
T S AIRLINE
IMPEL S G N
O O  L   H
NITTYGRITTY
```

243

```
REBUFF AMMO
O O I   O U
BJORN DEBUT
O T G I I E
TILLERS L N
  E R T E
R G TRUMPET
E G  I R H E
CHIRP BROOM
A N   E N P
POGO ADVERT
```

244
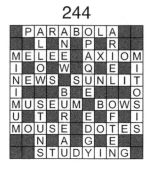

```
 PARABOLA
 L  N  P R
MELEE AXIOM
I O W Q E I
NEWS SUNLIT
I  B E F I O
MUSEUM BOWS
U T R E F  I
MOUSE DOTES
 N A G E
 STUDYING
```

245

```
O MICROCHIP
MOO O V O R
N PROSECUTE
I  P R R L
SAUCEPANS I
C  R C  M
I SPAGHETTI
E I T I  N
NEGLIGENT A
C H V OUR R
EXTREMELY Y
```

246

```
VEGETARIAN
A  I  A N
LUPIN FACET
I R G T I A
DEEMED FLAB
 M D F L
BLAB BEHALF
I T N N R E
BRUTE CRYPT
R X E  C
SEETHROUGH
```

247

```
 EJECTION
 O H N  A
TILDE DISCO
A L F I T A
GUYS LAWYER
G  A N  S
INGEST WHIM
N U C E O A
GLIDE APRON
 S N R S
 ENDANGER
```

248

```
GAPED  I G
U I  ROMEO
TREE S P O
 C STIPEND
BEA R  B
ANONYMOUSLY
D F M  O E
DECODER N
E A R TAXI
BAKED  T V
T E  PIETY
```

249

```
 S CAUSTIC
DITTO W  O
 O MILITIA
STRAP M  L
I I L A G E
DINNERDRESS
E G X O T C
S E  PLACE
HARVEST W
O E  EXALT
WHIRLED Y
```

250

```
A N P F A
BROTHERHOOD
O N E R E
VASES STEEP
E E H S T T
 NOURISH
S S T N O H
CHILD GAUZE
O C O G I
PLAYWRIGHTS
E L N T T
```

251

```
 BESMIRCH
 A I E A
EASEL HOIST
N E L A T H
LUSH ASSISI
I M H N
SCALAR MEAN
T D N S E
SPLAT ERROR
 I R N L
 BRANDISH
```

252

```
A B ITALIC
SPAIN A L
K N FAUXPAS
ANGEL N D
N I U O C J
CONTEMPLATE
E G N P B R
 H C OMITS
SADDENS N E
 L A EVERY
FABLED T S
```

Solutions

253

254
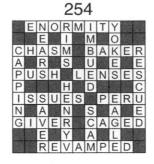

255

256

257

258

259

260

261

262

263

264

Solutions

265

```
V A L E D I C T I O N
  E       O   N     E
F N D   M A K E R
L I T H I U M   S   V
A   I   S   I       E
S E L F C O N T R O L
H   O   G   A       E
B   S   U P L I F T S
U P P E R   E   F   S
L   U   S       I
B U D G E R I G A R S
```

266

```
F   A   K   B   E
J U G G E R N A U T S
O   R   A   L   T
R U I N S   P U L S E
D   C   U   S   E   R
    U P S T A R T
F   L   P   C   P   S
L I T H E   K A R M A
U   U   C   O   S
M E R I T O R I O U S
P   E   S       F   Y
```

267

```
A N T I C I P A T E S
I   A   O   Y   E   O
M A R I N E R   A   U
        C   O S C A R
B I N G O   T   H   C
R   O   M   E   E   E
E   V   I   C O R D S
A V E R T   H
K   L   A N N U A L S
U   N   I   I   I   P
P R A C T I C A L L Y
```

268

```
  A   B E S E E C H
M O C H A   R   O
  T   I R O N I N G
M O R A L   E   S
O   E   O A K   H
D I S T U R B A N C E
I   S   T   Y   O A
F   H   S E W E D
I N D U C E S   H
E   M   A W O K E
D E S P O I L   W
```

269

```
I N S T A N C E S
  A   L   A   W
J U M B O   N O O S E
A   E   H   D   O
C   A M O U N T S
K   A   A   S   I
P A S S A G E   G
O   P   L   V   O N
T R E A T   E D G E S
  C   E   N   L
  T H R E S H E R S
```

270

```
I N D E P E N D E N T
C   E   R   E   N   R
Y A W N I N G   A   A
        C   O X B O W
W R E C K   T   L   L
A   N   L   I   E   E
T   V   Y   A L D E R
C H E E P   T
H   L   E P I T A P H
E   O   A   O   Y   A
S U P E R I N T E N D
```

271

```
P   B L I N D F O L D
R I A   N   E   B   I
O   N A S T I N E S S
G   I   F   S   O
R E C O N C I L E   B
E   E   U   C       E
S   U N A B A S H E D
S   S   T   T       I
I M A G I N I N G   E
V   G   N   O   U R N
E M E R G E N C Y   T
```

272

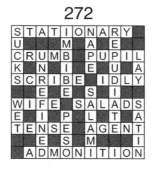

```
S T A T I O N A R Y
U   M   A   E
C R U M B   P U P I L
K   N   I   E   U   A
S C R I B E   I D L Y
    E   E S   I
W I F E   S A L A D S
E   I   P   L   T   A
T E N S E   A G E N T
    E   S   M       I
A D M O N I T I O N
```

273

```
B R A N D N A M E
E   N       I   A
C A N A D A   G E N E
A   E   U   H   T
U   L   S C A T T E R
S   I   T   A   A
E N D E M I C   M   M
  O   M   O   A   B
C O U P   N E U R A L
  K   T       I   E
  E Y E O P E N E R
```

274

```
A   A   M A R V E L
D U B A I   A   O
M   I   S O R T I N G
I D L E D   E   E
R   I   I   G   E   T
A F T E R B U R N E R
L   Y   E   L   T   A
  C   C   A I R E D
R O O S T E R   U   E
  W   I   L O S E R
L U X U R Y   T   S
```

275

```
D I S S I M I L A R
  N   N   E   E
A N T I   C L E A V E
  A   F   O   C
P R E F I X   H O C K
  D           H
I S I S   V I S U A L
    T   I   T   T
U P T A K E   A P E X
  I   R       L   A
E X T R A N E O U S
```

276

```
S E I S M O L O G Y
A   E   A   E   R
L I B Y A   S C O O P
E   O   N   H   U   O
S C O W L S   K N A P
    B   Y   D   D
D A Y S   V A R I E S
A   T   G   N   N   P
M E R C Y   C I G A R
  A   M   E       E
A P O S T R O P H E
```

Solutions

277

G	A	R	R	U	L	O	U	S		
R		I				M		S		
A	S	S	U	M	E		B	R	A	Y
P		I		P		R		R		
H		B		T	I	T	A	N	I	C
I		L		T		I		O		U
C	H	E	R	O	O	T		B		R
	E		H	M		B		B		R
C	L	A	Y		E	A	G	L	E	S
	D		M			E		E		E
		D	E	L	I	V	E	R	E	D

278

P	O	L	I	C	E	W	O	M	A	N
A		A		H		H		A		A
Y		Y		A	M	I	A	B	L	Y
M	O	D	E	L		T				
E		O		L		E	L	I	Z	A
N		W		E		C		N		L
T	E	N	O	N		O		S		T
		G			L	I	T	R	E	
S	P	A	N	I	E	L		A		R
E		N		N		A	N	E		E
E	X	A	G	G	E	R	A	T	E	D

279

P				G	I	N	G	H	A	M
R	O	U	T		A		I		E	
O		N		F		U		S	O	N
J		D	R	O	U	G	H	T		T
E		E		R		H		O		A
C	O	N	J	E	C	T	U	R	A	L
T		I		I		I		I		B
I		A	N	G	E	L	I	C		L
L	A	B		N		Y		A		O
E		L		E			B	L	O	C
S	M	E	A	R	E	D				K

280

C	O	P	P	E	R	F	I	E	L	D
O		A		X		U		A		U
M		R		P	E	N	G	U	I	N
M	O	T	T	E		D				
A		I		N		A	P	P	A	L
N		A		D		M		R		A
D	E	L	H	I		E		I		W
			T		N	E	V	I	S	
D	E	F	A	U	L	T		A		U
E		I		R		A		T		I
C	O	N	C	E	A	L	M	E	N	T

281

D	I	S	A	P	P	E	A	R	E	D
E		U		A		N		A		R
N	U	M	E	R	A	L		D		U
			T		I	D	I	O	M	
B	A	S	I	N		G		A		M
E		T		E		H		N		E
A		O		R		T	U	T	O	R
R	A	I	L	S		E				
D		C		H	A	N	D	F	U	L
E		A		I		E		I		I
D	I	L	A	P	I	D	A	T	E	D

282

C	A	P	I	T	A	L	I	S	T	
O		A		O		P				
W	O	M	E	N		S	H	A	R	P
E		A		N		E		R		E
R	A	N	C	I	D		S	K	I	P
I		N		H		L				
B	U	F	F		T	A	R	I	F	F
O		E		J		T		N		U
P	A	S	T	E		T	O	G	A	S
		T		E		E		S		S
C	O	M	P	A	R	A	B	L	Y	

283

S		F		E			D		A	
M	A	L	E	D	I	C	T	I	O	N
O		E		I		S			O	
C	L	E	A	T		D	A	T	E	D
K		T		I		E		I		E
		S	H	O	W	M	A	N		
H		T		N		O		G		C
A	C	R	E	S		T	R	U	T	H
N		E				I		I		O
G	R	E	E	N	H	O	U	S	E	S
S		T		N		H		E		

284

S		F			P	C		I		
T	R	E	A	C	H	E	R	O	U	S
U		A		N		M		L		
B	O	T	C	H		G	O	R	G	E
S		U		O		U		A		T
		R	E	S	C	I	N	D		
S		E		T		N		E		P
H	A	L	V	E		S	I	S	A	L
A		E		L				H		U
D	I	S	T	R	E	S	S	I	N	G
Y		S		Y				P		S

285

F	A	R	R	E	A	C	H	I	N	G
L		E		L		A		A		A
U		C		E	X	T	E	N	D	S
S	T	O	I	C		E				
T		U		T		R	O	G	E	R
E		N		R		P		L		E
R	A	T	I	O		I		I		A
			N		L	I	M	E	S	
N	U	P	T	I	A	L		P		O
E		E		C		A		S		N
W	I	N	D	S	C	R	E	E	N	S

286

P			P	A	R	A	D	E	D	
R	U	D	E		E		E		A	
E		I	N		S		P	I	N	
R		S	T	E	R	I	L	E		G
E		R		U	D		N		E	
C	H	E	E	R	L	E	A	D	E	R
O		S		A		N		E		O
R		P	E	L	I	C	A	N		U
D	O	E		G		E		C		S
E		C		I		R	E	A	L	
D	E	T	R	A	C	T				Y

287

	E	S	P	R	E	S	S	O		
		H		E		P		R		
A	M	I	D	E		H	A	I	K	U
L		R		D		I		B		N
A	C	T	S		E	N	R	I	C	H
R			R		M	X		A		A
M	E	D	I	A	L		P	O	M	P
E		R		D		R		S		P
D	R	A	K	E		E	D	I	F	Y
		F		U		D		E		
	T	A	P	E	S	T	R	Y		

288

B	R	O	A	D	M	I	N	D	E	D
U		U		E		L		E		I
D	U	T	I	F	U	L		S		N
		E		U	N	P	I	N		
S	U	P	E	R		S		A		E
T		A		E		I		I		R
A		R		N		O	G	R	E	S
R	I	V	E	T		N				
T		E		I	M	I	T	A	T	E
L		N		A		S		I		E
E	Q	U	I	L	A	T	E	R	A	L

Solutions

289

```
C R E S C E N D O
  V     A   E   R
P L E A S   R A G E D
R   S     E   V A R
O         S T E R N L Y
B   S     I     S   N
L I M P O P O       E
E   I   U   U   C   S
M O T E T   G A L L S
    E   E   H   O
    S T R A T A G E M
```

290

```
H O R R O R F I L M
U     B     E   J
M O L E S   T H U M B
P   O     E   B   U
S P L A S H   P L A Y
    L     S   S   J
H A I L   S P R A N G
U   P   O   R   N   R
B L O O M   A M A Z E
    P   A   I     A
A S T R I N G E N T
```

291

```
A   C O M M A N D E R
T A U   A   B   R   E
M   T R I L O G I E S
O     N   M   V   P
S O L I T A I R E   O
P     E   N     N
H   T E N T A C L E S
E   E     A   T     I
R E M I N D I N G   B
I   P   C   O   O I L
C L O S E K N I T   E
```

292

```
M O N T E C A R L O
  V   R     U   A
Z E T A   R E M A K E
  R   D     A   M
A L B E I T   Y A R D
  I             H
R E A M   A D A G I O
  I   W   T   Z
S H E L V E   O B O E
  O   L     M   M
B U S I N E S S E S
```

293

```
  A   H A P P E N S
R A D I O   E     H
  A   R E T S I N A
P A P E R   T   M
R   T   I   A Q B
I N E F F E C T U A L
N   D   Y   C I E
C   P     L E E R S
E C H I D N A   T
  L   E     I N L A W
Y T T R I U M   Y
```

294

```
S   P   H I C C U P
W E E D Y     A   U
I   N   P R O B I T Y
L A S S O   P     T
L   I   C E   P   A
E N V I R O N M E N T
D   E   I   E   R T
    V   T   N O V A E
S E A W E E D   A N
  E   A   E N D E D
R H Y M E D   E   S
```

295

```
S U C H   S M U D G E
A   O     A   I   A
V I N Y L   K I N G S
E   D   E   E   N E
D   I   M I S D E E D
    T   O   H   R
C H I A N T I   P   M
A   O   S   F   A A
K E N D O   T A R R Y
E   A   L     T   B
S A L T E D   L Y R E
```

296

```
  O M I T T I N G
    A   O   M   H
W O R D Y   P R O S E
A   I   S   U   X
V I A L   S T A T I C
E     S   E     U
L A R V A E   A C E S
E   O   W   O O   E
T A L L Y   W O R K S
  E   E   E   A
  S P R I N K L E
```

297

```
B   L   C       A   G
Y O U T H H O S T E L
W   X   I       T   A
A D U L T   P L E A D
Y   R   C   U   S   E
    I N H I B I T
S   A   A   L   A   R
T E N E T   I N T R O
A   T   C   I   U
M E L L I F L U O U S
P   Y   Y       N   E
```

298

```
C   S E L E C T I O N
A R K   I   O   C   E
T   I N T E R D I C T
A   H   P   L   H
C O S M O L O G Y   E
L     S   R     R
Y   A P P R A I S A L
S   R   H   T     A
M I S B E L I E F   N
I   O   R   O   A D D
C O N D E M N E D   S
```

299

```
  T   A D A M A N T
C R A M P   O   R
  R   P R O V I S O
D R I L L   E   U
R   F   A   E M B
I N F L U E N T I A L
Z   S   D   C S E
Z   F   R A F T S
L O Y A L T Y   I
E   I     P U T T S
D E F R O S T   S
```

300

```
A B R A C A D A B R A
  H     E   O   M
B Y A   P R U N E
L I T E R A L   T   N
A   H   B   E     I
C O M P O R T M E N T
K     R   I   L   I
B   M E M O T I V E
E X A C T   N   C S
L   N     U   I
T H E R M O M E T E R
```

Solutions

301

```
P A I L   P L A C E R
R N     I   H   A
O P T I C   G R O W S
B O   E   H   L   P
E L   L O T T E R Y
    E     E   B   S
C A R I B O U   T   A
A A   R   L   E   L
M A N T A   B U R N T
E C   T       O   A
O B E Y E D   B L U R
```

302

```
E T   R E A R E D
P U R E E   A   U
I I   C O P Y I S T
S P R A T   R   T
O E   A   E P   A
D I M I N I S H I N G
E E G   E M   I
  P   L   N E P A L
S U B J E C T   L   I
  R A   E V E R T
R I B B E D   S   Y
```

303

```
I     R E D U C E D
N O U N   E   A   E
T   N S S   R U M
O   E N A C T E D   O
L   X   N   I   I
E X P E D I T I O N S
R E   P   U G   T
A   C L A T T E R   A
B U T   P   E   A
L E E   E   S M U T E
E N D U R E S     E
```

304

```
  C O N F I N E D
    W   U   E O
W H I Z Z   A S P I C
A   N   Z R   E   A
T U G S   P L A Y E R
E   O   Y       R
R A R E F Y   M I N I
E   I   F   E D   E
D U C K S   B R O A D
    C   E   O   L
    I N T E R E S T
```

305

```
A   A     S H   G
B I F U R C A T I O N
U   F     T   B A
Z A I R E   I N E R T
Z   R M A   R   S
    M O I S T E N
A   A   S   E   A D
M I T E S   D E T E R
A   I   A   I   I A
S O V E R E I G N T Y
S   E   Y     G   S
```

306

```
M     C O N C E A L
O A T H   O   L   I
L   O   H   T   E G O
Y   U N I F O R M   N
C   R   B   R   E H
C O N V E N I E N C E
O   A   R   E   T   R
D   M I N U T I A   T
D U E   A   Y   R   T
L   N   T   B Y T E
E N T R E A T     D
```

307

```
L E A D E R S H I P
  C   E     A   R
D O L L   H O T D O G
  L   F   O   C
B O T T L E   H I D E
  G           E
E Y E S   V E N I C E
      T   A   A   O
A B S E I L   D I R T
  I   A   A   U
  N O M D E P L U M E
```

308

```
S I S T E R I N L A W
W   C   X   N Y   I
A   H   P A T I E N T
L I E G E   E
L   R   R   L O A D S
O   Z I L   P   E
W R I T E   I R   T
      N   G U I L T
P A N A C H E   O   I
U   U   E N   R   N
B A B Y S I T T I N G
```

309

```
O   B   A     B   S
V I R I D E S C E N T
A   O   O     L   U
L I N E R   D Y L A N
S   Z   A I   B   T
    E M B A R G O
B   M   L E   T   S
R E E V E   C U T U P
A   D     T   O   U
T R A N S F O R M E D
S   L     R   S   S
```

310

```
D I S R E S P E C T S
R   C   X   R   O   E
A   A   T H O U G H T
S O N A R   B
T   D   A   L A G E R
I   A   P   E   O   E
C E L L O   M   N   D
    L   A D D O N
  S E R V A N T   O   E
A   A   T   I   L   S
C O M M E R C I A L S
```

311

```
R A C E T R A C K
  A   U   L   E
R I V E N   I N L A Y
E   Y   I   E   V   I
F   C O N N I V E   E
U   F   R   N   L
G A L I L E O     D
E   E   U   T X E
E I D E R   H U M I D
  G   E   E   E
  E N S H R I N E S
```

312

```
P E N I C I L L I N
A   I     O   S
C O M E T   G R O U P
T   A   I   S   M   S
S I G N E D   S E M I
    A   S   S   T
J A Z Z   S C A R E S
A   I   S   A   I   E
M U N C H   R A C E R
    E   O   A     G
A S S E M B L A G E
```

Solutions

313

```
I U C H E W E D
C A N T O   O   A
E   U   W I C K E T S
P A S T A   O   E
I   U   R   N   L   D
C L A N D E S T I N E
K   L   I   E   F   P
  G   C   N A T A L
P L A Y E R S   O   E
  U   A   U N F I T
M A K E R S   F   E
```

314

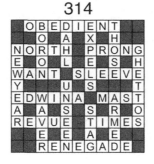

```
  O B E D I E N T
  O   A   X   H
N O R T H   P R O N G
E   O   L   E   S   H
W A N T   S L E E V E
Y   U   S   T
E D W I N A   M A S T
A   A S   S   R   O
R E V U E   T I M E S
  E   E   A   E
  R E N E G A D E
```

315

```
D I S Q U A L I F Y
I   P   I   R
V A P I D   S N E E R
A   A   I   P E   I
S T R I K E   F L A G
  A   E   T   A
J U G S   C O G N A C
I   R   W   B   C   A
G L A Z E   A R E A S
  P   A   G   E
C H A R D O N N A Y
```

316

```
S   D   S     C   I
P R E S T I G I O U S
A   S   A   M   A
R A T E D   G A M M A
E   I   I   A   U   C
  T H U R M A N
A   U   M   B   I   F
M E T E S   L O T T O
B   I   I   I   S
I R O N M O N G E R S
T   N   G   S   E
```

317

```
J   U   B   T   S
I M P E R T I N E N T
F   S   R   M   E
F R A U D   T A P E R
Y   N   I   H   E   N
  D I V I D E R
C   D   I   A   A   K
L O O P S   Y E M E N
U   W   I   E   E
B E N E V O L E N C E
S   S   E   T   S
```

318

```
C O N T A I N E R S
O   V   O   E
D I R G E   S L I N G
E   E   R   E   T   O
R E P U T E   H E R B
  R   S   B   R
C A I N   S A V A N T
A   E   F   S   T   A
D E V I L   S K E I N
  E   O   E   K
A D V E N T U R E S
```

319

```
C O W O R K E R S
E   E   O   C
D E L E T E   P R O D
I   L   S   E   M
L   O   S T A S H E D
L   F   A   U   E
A F F E C T S   T   C
  L   A   E   C   I
B E R G   S I G H E D
A   E   E   E
  P R O F E S S E D
```

320

```
T S H I R T   A R C H
U   E   A   E   A
L E A S T   S A V V Y
I   V   I   E   E   E
P A Y L O A D   R   K
  H   N   E   E
F   A   A W N I N G S
E   N   L   T   T   W
L A D L E   A B I D E
O   E   R   A   A
N O D E   E Y E L E T
```

321

```
D U M B F O U N D S
  S   R   A   H
A U R A   G A D G E T
  R   V   A   I
A P L O M B   R A N D
E   E   U
O D E S   O V E R D O
  H   P   V   G
F I N E S T   E D I T
M   A   N   N
P E R C E N T A G E
```

322

```
  U   P O L E N T A
H A N O I   Y   L
  C   C A R E F U L
C H A R T   D   I
Y   N   U   S   D   A
C O N T R A P T I O N
L   Y   E   I   F   C
A   S   R I F L E
M A S C A R A   E
E   A   L U R C H
N I B B L E S   S
```

323

```
S   H   L     P   M
P R E P A R A T O R Y
I   A   T   L   T
C O V E T   P A T C H
E   Y   E   O   E   S
  W A R B L E R
S   E   L   Y   G   G
L A I T Y   G R E E R
O   G   L   I   E
T C H A I K O V S K Y
S   T   T   T   S
```

324

```
C   T   P U F F E D
E Q U A L   I   A
N   R   A C E R B I C
T E M P I   P   S
R   O   N   I   B   M
A R I S T O C R A C Y
L   L   I   U   G   S
E   F   R I G H T
S C U F F L E   A   E
H   R   A N G E R
O X Y G E N   E   Y
```

Solutions

325

```
R E C O N D I T E
E L   U   F
T E A S E S   S P A N
R   S   H   K   N
A   S   C O N S I S T
C   I   W   N   R
T I C K L E D   S   A
  B   A R   P   C
F I Z Z   S E V E R E
  S   O       C   R
  C O M P A C T L Y
```

326

```
I M P R E S S I O N S
  A     C V   E
B   T S   U N I T E
L Y R I C A L   D   M
U   O   R   P     I
N O N P A R T I S A N
D     P   U   A   G
E   V   H U R T F U L
R A I S E   E   A   Y
E   S   A       R
R E A P P O R T I O N
```

327

```
R   A N A E R O B I C
H E N   C   E R   O
O   D E C E P T I O N
D     E   L   D   F
E X C U L P A T E   O
I       E   C     U
S   P O R C E L A I N
L   O   A   M     D
A L L O T M E N T   I
N K   O   N     I N N
D I A C R I T I C   G
```

328

```
A   S     C   I   B
S M A L L C H A N G E
K   V     E   D   R
E X I S T   S A U C Y
W   N   H   S   S   L
    G R O M M E T
S   G   U   E   R   D
P A R T S   N A I V E
A   A   A   O   L
D E C O N S T R U C T
E   E   D     S   A
```

329

```
S   D   B     D   G
P R O G R E S S I O N
U   W   O     S   A
R E N E W   C A P E R
T   T   B   L   O   L
    O P E N E R S
S   E   A   M   I   I
Q U A R T   E L T O N
U   R   N   I   L
A N T I C Y C L O N E
T   H     Y   N   T
```

330

```
A F T E R S H O C K
B     E   A   H
A D A G E   S C A R F
S   P   K   P   L   I
H O P P E D   G L I B
    A   D   P   E
J U L Y   C L I N I C
A   L   G   A   G   A
G R I M E   T W E E D
    N   A   E   G
A G G R E S S I V E
```

331

```
P A S S E D   E M I R
A   E   S   A   U
P U L L S   W A L L S
A   F   E   H   E   K
L I C E N C E   V   S
    E   T   T   O
G   N   I N S U L T S
A   T   A   T   E   H
M E R Y L   O U N C E
U   E   N   C   E
T I D Y   D E M E A N
```

332

```
C     D E D U C E D
A R T Y   A   O   E
M   E   P   R   N E T
A   L A R D E R S   E
R   E   I   D   C   R
A B S E N T E E I S M
D   C   C   V   E   I
E   O P I N I O N   N
R I P P   L   C   A
I   E   A   F E E T
E P S I L O N     E
```

333

```
U R S A M A J O R
  K   A   U   O
S L I N K   N O U N S
O   N   E   T   N   T
U   S L A N D E R
F   A   A   S   A
F O L L O W S     T
L   B   V   E   G   U
E T U D E   V E I L S
  M   R   E   F
S A T U R A T E D
```

334

```
D   S T U T T E R E D
E M U   N   H   O   E
T   N E F A R I O U S
E     O   E   M   P
R A I L R O A D S   O
M     T   T   N
I   H O U S E H O L D
N   A   N   N   E
I M I T A T I O N   N
S   R   T   N   O R C
M E S S E N G E R   Y
```

335

```
D I P S   T E N D E R
E   E   M   E   I
B E R E T   O R C A S
U   S   O   T   E   E
G   E   O R I G I N S
    C   T   O   V
T O U G H E N   I   L
E   T   L   A   N   A
A F I R E   L I G H T
C   O   S       L   E
H O N E S T   L Y N X
```

336

```
U       S I M P L E R
N E A T   I   I   E
C   S   R   S   K E G
O   T R E A C L E   R
N   U   V   H   M   E
N A T I O N A L I S T
E   E   L   N   N   T
C   N O T I C E D   A
T E E   I   E   B
E   S   N   I D O L
D E S I G N S     E
```

Solutions

337

```
  K CASTING
DINGO   E  R
  E NOTABLE
CLEFT   K  N
A  C  A  A  A
PLAYINGCARD
S  P  N  I  E
I  I  D  TRUSS
COCHLEA  R
U  O  TREES
MIDWIFE  S
```

338

```
CENTIMETRE
O  N  A  E
MUTED STAFF
E  R  I  S L
STARCH MONO
   D  T R N
ARIA DOTING
S  T B  N E
KNIFE BEGIN
  O D E   I
 UNBEARABLE
```

339

```
DERIDE LIED
U  E A   N U
TALKS  SETTS
C  U T P E T
HECTARE  R S
   T R C E
S  A DETESTS
I  N L  A T U
NATTY  TRIED
E  L   O N A
WHYS DRAGON
```

340

```
B WEARINESS
ASH  C  N  O
T YOUNGSTER
  P  R R  C
LEISURELY  E
  N  D  R
F MACHINATE
I  O  E   S
ELOQUENCE  S
L  N  R T LEE
DISPERSAL  S
```

341

```
JERUSALEM
  I  L A I
CAPRI  TONIC
A E D H U  A
R  EJECTOR
A A O  E V
MARIMBA   E
E D  E R T R
LOOSE IRONY
  U  T E G
 RESISTANT
```

342

```
DODGER SMUG
O  I T   I O
ZESTY DINAR
E  T M I D S
NARROWS  B E
   I L T L
D B ORATORS
U U G N W T
KITTY CLIVE
E O   E N P
SURE ADAGES
```

343

```
BUREAUCRACY
E U F A E  O
TONIGHT  R U
  H  AGAIN
CIRCA S T  G
U A N T E E
L I I RADAR
TENDS O
U  I TYPICAL
R N A H H E
ENGINEERING
```

344

```
DESERVING
E I   I C
VIRILE EMUS
I O  X C R
O C STEEPLE
  C  R L N
STOPGAP  A O
 R I  C U
VEST TUREEN
 K H   B C
 XYLOPHONE
```

345

```
MICROSCOPE
U  P O  R
LATTE SEOUL
E H N T  C O
SKILLS VENT
 N Y R D
YAKS FUTURE
E A D B R S
SOBER REEFS
  L O I  A
DESPICABLY
```

346

```
S  N  O C S
CHOCKABLOCK
O U  S M  I
WORLD TIMER
L I R R I T
 STATUES
S H M C E S
MUMBA THREW
A E T  A A
CONFIDENTLY
K T C  E S
```

347

```
S P A  P F
COUNTERFOIL
U B T L I
DELVE PAYEE
S I N A T S
 CADENCE
C H E D C A
AVOID ETHIC
N U  M N H
INSENSITIVE
S E  C C S
```

348

```
F C  S E R
INHERITANCE
E I  I C U
FORTH MOODS
S O E U U E
 PEDDLER
C O G U A A
LEDGE SAGAS
O R  I K
DISCONTINUE
S T W  G D
```

Solutions

349
```
C O N S T R U C T E D
U   I   R   N   H   E
E M P T I E D   R   C
    C   E R O D E   N
O V A T E   R   N   N
R   R   R   W   G   C
I   R   A   R I S K Y
G L I N T   I
A   V   O U T W O R K
M   A   P E A   I
I L L U S T R A T E D
```

350
```
P A L I N D R O M E
E   E   U   I
S C R E W   C E D A R
T   E   T   K   W   E
S Y M B O L   T I F F
    I   N   M   C
J U N E   R A C K E T
O   I   A   E   I
T Y S O N   L A T I N
    C   N   E   G
D E L E C T A B L E
```

351
```
  P A N O R A M A
  U   N   B   S
P I X E L   J U L E P
O   I   Y   U   A
P E N S   K R O N E R
U   S   E   F
L I S T E D   E Z R A
A   T   X   B E I
R O O S T   A B B O T
    M   O   I   R
  P U N C T U A L
```

352
```
    M   V I N T N E R
G A U G E   A   E
    S   N E G L E C T
B L E E D   E   A
A   U   O   U R I
C O M P R E S S I O N
I   S   S   U N E
L   T   A U G E R
L O G I C A L   I
U   E   L E N D S
S H A R P L Y   G
```

353
```
B R A H M S   U S E S
A   G E   U   A
S T O R M   R E F E R
E   R O E   F A
D I A G R A M   I H
  P   A A C
P H   B A I L I F F
A O L   N E A
S A B R E   D O N O R
S I   E C A
E A C H   P R E Y E D
```

354
```
W O O D W O R K E R
H   A   O   N
A B H O R   A U D I O
C   A   R D L D
K E R N E L   M E T E
  M   N P S
B R O W   C R I S P Y
I N C   E L A
D R I E R   F O Y E R
C I E D
H A M B U R G E R S
```

355
```
G E R B I L   T S A R
L   O   N   C A
Y A C H T   L O H A N
P   K   R I O T
H E A R I N G   O S
  N C H L
A D   A N T I G E N
P R T Y   I U
P R O N E   E R R E D
L L   A L G
Y O L K   W R A S S E
```

356
```
L E P R E C H A U N
O   R   Y   N
C E L L S   P O W E R
H   O   A E I E
S Q U A T S   A L G A
  I Z C L
W I S P   S O D I U M
O I D N   N A
W E A R Y   T I G E R
  N E R   G
R A M S H A C K L E
```

357
```
L   A   C O L D E R
A P P L E   U   A
P   P   L O D G I N G
T R O P E   E   T
O   I S F M A
P U N C T I L I O U S
S   T I E N P
  F   A   C A D R E
C O U P L E T   A C
U A   E G Y P T
R E W A R D   S S
```

358
```
G     S H A K E U P
R E S T   B   M E
A A G H   B A R
S   C O R P O R A   S
S R O R N O
H E A R T B R O K E N
O M E E M A
P   E S S E N C E   L
P U N Q T N I
E T U   S T E T
R E S P E C T   Y
```

359
```
A   P A S S P O R T S
P H I   Y R A U
H   G O N D O L I E R
R   D L N R
O F F L I M I T S   O
D   C F U
I   S T A T E S M A N
S U T R D
I N S T I G A T E   I
A H O T   K I N
C L I E N T E L E G
```

360
```
S   L   T I C K E R
A R I S E   E   I
N Z   M A D N E S S
C L A M P   E   K
T R E S U O
U N D E R S T A N D S
M S A R I P
B T   O C C U R
V E L V E T Y O E
A E   E A R L Y
M A T T E D   N S
```

Solutions

361

```
  U   S K Y H I G H
S O N I C       A   O
  A   O U T W E A R
H E W E R   K       N
E   A   P   O       B
P E R M I S S I B L E
T   E   O   M   L A
A   T   O D I U M
G L O W E R S   G
O   I     I D E A L
N A N N I E S   D
```

362

```
S     S E C U R E D
A C H E   L   E   E
U   I A E   S I P   R
D   E N L A R G E   R
I   R M G N E       E
A P O C A L Y P T I C
R   G M M M       A
A   L E A K A G E   T
B O Y   T   N   N   I
I   P E     S T U N
A D H E R E S     G
```

363

```
    F   C A D M I U M
R O U T E     A     O
    L   L E X I C O N
L I S P S   N       S
O   O   I   D   R   T
C O M M U N I C A T E
H   E   S   O   M   R
N   A   C U B E S
E D I F I C E   L
S   A   S H E D S
S U P R E M E   S
```

364

```
D U M B F O U N D
  A   L   R   A
A M I G O   G I R T H
X   L   R   E I E
O   A B S E N C E   D
L   L   O   G   D
O V E R L A P       F
T   M U   A H U
L U M E N   G R I L L
  A   A   E   S
  S U R P R I S E D
```

365

```
S Q       C   D   S
C O U N T E R F E I T
O   A     E   M   E
F I R E D   D R O N E
F   R   R   I G D
    E L E C T O R
A   L S O   A   F
B A S I S   R E P E L
O   O E     H   A
D E M A R C A T I O N
E   E S     C   K
```

366

```
G A T E C R A S H E R
L   O   L   S U O   O
I   N   O C T A G O N
D I G I T   R
I   U   H   O L S E N
N   E E N   A   E
G U S T S   O T A
        L   M O I S T
R E J O I C E   A   E
U   E N   R   T   S
B I T T E R S W E E T
```

Printed in Great Britain
by Amazon